The 12 Step Workbook:

A Guided Journey

Through the Twelve Steps

of Addiction Recovery

The 12 Step Workbook

A Guided Journey Through the Twelve Steps of Addiction Recovery

www.12stepjournals.com

Help us reach others who would benefit from this book by leaving a review on Amazon (if purchased there) or on our website: www.12stepjournals.com

Published by Alver Valley Press

Printed in China

First Edition 2021

ISBN: 978-1-9165059-1-9

Contents

Introduction

Welcome ♦ How to use this workbook ♦ Fellowship contacts
Your story ♦ The Twelve Steps

Step One

Step Two

Step Three

Step Four

Step Five

Step Six

Step Seven

Step Eight

Step Nine

Step Ten

Step Eleven

Step Twelve

Notes & Reflections

Blank pages for: ♦ extra space ♦ notes ♦ reflections

> 66
>
> *There is a solution. Almost none of us liked the self-searching, the levelling of our pride, the confession of shortcomings which the process requires for its successful consummation. But we saw that it really worked in others, and we had come to believe in the hopelessness and futility of life as we had been living it. When, therefore, we were approached by those in whom the problem had been solved, there was nothing left for us but to pick up the simple kit of spiritual tools laid at our feet. We have found much of heaven and we have been rocketed into a forth dimension of existence of which we had not even dreamed.*

Alcoholics Anonymous. (2001). *Alcoholics Anonymous, 4th Edition*. New York: A.A. World Services. p.25. (AKA 'The Big Book of AA').

Welcome

A very warm and heartfelt welcome, fellow travellers. What you're holding in your hands has been lovingly created in the hope of helping you on your journey of transformation, away from addiction and towards serenity. We want you to succeed and we are with you.

Some of you reading this are new to Twelve Step recovery. You may be nervous about what's ahead, angry that you have to resort to this, afraid it won't work. You may be at your rock bottom. To you, we say Welcome. You are so welcome here. We've all been where you are, and please know that we are with you now. Our hope is that the guidance in these pages, along with that of your sponsor, fellowship and literature, engage you and bring to life the essence of each and every step.

Some of you are returning to the Twelve Steps, after a relapse or from time away from the program. There may be a sense of resignation, of *here we go again.* To you we say Welcome. Well done for coming back, we know it really took something for you to get back here and we acknowledge you for that. Our hope is that this workbook helps you rediscover your passion for recovery and living a better life.

Some of you have a long history of successful recovery and maintain your spiritual condition by repeatedly working through the steps, always peeling back more and more layers of the metaphorical onion. To you we say Welcome. We recognize your tenacity and are inspired by the example you set. Our hope is that these pages add fuel to your ongoing journey of growth and surrender.

And some of you have taken on the role of sponsor, offering your time and energy in service of the recovery of others. To you we say Welcome. We were all guided through the Twelve Steps by someone like you, someone who saw something in us that we couldn't see ourselves. We thank you and we acknowledge you. Our hope is that this workbook can serve as a useful tool to use with your sponsees, as well as in your ongoing recovery.

To all of you, Welcome. Our hope is that this workbook will create structure, grounding and a single place for all your step work — something to be looked back on in the years to come and cherished. If you become a sponsor in the future, it'll help to remind you of where you were and what you were dealing with when you first worked the steps, helping you share yourself and connect with your sponsees more effectively.

We would truly love to hear about your experiences with this workbook—your questions, comments and suggestions for improvement. All will be gratefully received and replied to, as we continually strive to serve you better. Get in touch: recovery@12stepjournals.com

The 12 Step Journals Team

How to use this workbook

What this workbook IS NOT

Firstly, it's important to get clear about what this workbook isn't. It is not a replacement for a sponsor. The idea of working through the steps alone is appealing to some of us, we think that if we just work hard enough, we won't need anyone to guide us through the work. But the experience of millions of recovered addicts tells us that this approach is doomed to fail.

Nor is this workbook a replacement for meetings, literature or fellowship. These remain fundamental and essential aspects of recovery that each of us have come to cherish. If we could recover without these things, many of us would have recovered long ago.

The workbook will not do the work for you. You won't find answers or shortcuts here, only themes for you to explore and discover for yourself.

And finally, this workbook certainly isn't *the definitive way* to work the steps. For there is no such thing. There are as many ways to work the steps as there are people in recovery. It is up to each of us to learn what works for us, under the guidance of our sponsor, others in recovery and our Higher Power.

What this workbook IS

This workbook has been created to be a tool to be used *with* your sponsor and alongside attending meetings, reading literature and participating in fellowship.

It has been designed to replace the tatty notebooks and loose worksheets so many of us are familiar with. It can be the single place where all your written step work can be done.

The workbook encourages you to write things down rather than just think about them and try and remember them. It provides an overarching structure to the work, that ensures the principles underlying each step are fully explored, for these principles are the keys to our freedom.

The workbook can serve as the documentation of your personal journey of transformation—something to be looked back on and cherished. Those of us who go on to be a sponsor in the future will be able to clearly see where we were in life when we worked the steps, what we were dealing with — for this can be all too easy to forget. This clarity will help us understand, relate to, and really *be with* those we sponsor.

What the workbook contains

Each of the Twelve Steps has it's own section to be worked through before moving onto the next step. Questions, and where appropriate, specific exercises and inventories, form the guidance that carries us through the steps, making sure no stone is left unturned as we work towards lasting recovery.

Each step also contains quotes and prayers from approved literature from various Twelve Step fellowships, to provide a solid grounding for our work. And each step ends with a completion page, where we agree with our sponsor that we have completed this step and are ready to move onto the next.

On the next few pages, before Step One, there is space to start compiling a growing list of people to stay in touch with, as well as a place to write out your personal history of addiction— many of us find this very helpful to do at some stage in our recovery.

And at the back, after Step Twelve, there are plenty of blank pages to use for jotting down any notes and reflections that come up while working the steps. These pages can also be used if you need more space for a particular step.

Freedom and Flexibility

The Twelve Step Workbook has been carefully and lovingly designed to give you complete freedom to work the steps however you and your sponsor see fit. While specific questions, exercises and inventories are provided, you'll see that you are not in any way tied to them. They are there purely as guidance.

For example, the questions appear at the top, bottom or sides of the page, with blank space to use as you wish. It's all entirely flexible and adaptable. Questions can be answered, skipped or replaced under the guidance of your sponsor. And there are no restrictions on how you use the space on each page. We've allowed you to use as much or as little space for each answer as you need, rather than defining for you how long each answer should be.

This approach contrasts the traditional format of having a question followed by space for the answer, which forces you to follow someone else's pre-specified structure.

Why write it all down?

Working through the Twelve Steps is a journey of discovery. Insights and revelations come thick and fast, and at times this can be a little overwhelming and hard to process.

Many of us find that writing things down allows us to go deeper with our thoughts and reflections, producing deeper and longer lasting transformation. It can be difficult to keep things in our heads, trying to remember key points and separating valuable nuggets of gold from all the background faulty thinking.

For many of us, the act of writing down our step work brings clarity and helps us build a solid foundation for our recovery. While it can seem like a chore, many of us find the benefits it brings worth the effort, and are willing to commit to the practice.

A suggestion for how to use this workbook

We only recommend working through this workbook under the guidance of a caring sponsor. So if you haven't found one yet, our advice is simple: take the time, and perhaps a leap of faith, and find one – someone who has what you want.

At the start of each step, it can be good to sit down with your sponsor and talk about how you will work it. You can look through that section of the workbook and agree which of the questions, exercises and inventories would be beneficial for you to work through.

Your sponsor may have other work for you to do, either in addition or as a replacement for some of the content in this workbook. This may be other questions, exercises or activities, and will also likely include reading through some fellowship literature.

It can be good to agree a timeframe for you to have completed each part of the work, and you can then plan your time accordingly.

Once each part is complete, it's likely your sponsor will want to go through your work with you, discussing key points as you go.

When you and your sponsor both agree that a step has been completed, you can fill in the step completion page, before moving on to the next step.

66

After all, it is through sharing with each other that we find our own answers, our own Higher Power, and our own path of recovery

Narcotics Anonymous. (1993). *It Works, How and Why*. Chatsworth, California: Narcotics Anonymous World Services, Inc. p.2

Fellowship Contacts

Living in addiction usually isolates us. And this isolation feeds the addiction in a vicious cycle. Staying connected to people is an essential pillar in our recovery, one that can be all too easy to neglect, especially when we're feeling vulnerable. Use this page to list the people who make up your support network—those who maintaining a relationship with benefits you both. You may want to note their phone numbers as well. Keep adding to the list as other people come into your life. Maintaining this list reminds us to stay connected.

My Story

Many of us find it helpful, at some stage in our recovery, to write out our personal history of addiction. It can help us get clear in our minds how we ended up where we are today. Some people do this before or during Step 1, some as part of Step 5, some during another step, and some not at all.

_____

_____

_____

_____

_____

_____

_____

_____

_____

_____

_____

_____

_____

_____

_____

_____

_____

_____

_____

_____

_____

_____

My Story

My Story

My Story

My Story

Step One
We admitted we were powerless over our addiction, that our lives had become unmanageable

~

Step Two
We came to believe that a Power greater than ourselves could restore us to sanity

~

Step Three
We made a decision to turn our will and our lives over to the care of God as we understood Him

~

Step Four
We made a searching and fearless moral inventory of ourselves

~

Step Five
We admitted to God, to ourselves, and to another human being the exact nature of our wrongs

~

Step Six
We were entirely ready to have God remove all these defects of character

Step Seven

We humbly asked Him to remove our shortcomings

~

Step Eight

We made a list of all persons we had harmed and became willing to make amends to them all

~

Step Nine

We made direct amends to such people wherever possible, except when to do so would injure them or others

~

Step Ten

We continued to take personal inventory and when we were wrong promptly admitted it

~

Step Eleven

We sought through prayer and meditation to improve our conscious contact with God as we understood Him, praying only for knowledge of His will for us and the power to carry that out

~

Step Twelve

Having had a spiritual awakening as a result of these steps, we tried to carry this message to addicts and to practice these principles in all our affairs

Today, I ask for help with my addiction. Denial has kept me from seeing how powerless I am and how my life is unmanageable. I need to learn and remember that I have an incurable illness and that abstinence is the only way to deal with it.

First Step Prayer. Bill P. and Lisa D. *The 12 Step Prayer Book. 2nd ed*. Center City, Minn.: Hazelden, 2004

Step One

We admitted we were
powerless over our
addiction—that our lives
had become unmanageable

Guidance

* Use these pages in whichever way
  serves you best

* Feel free to answer the suggested
  questions at the top of the pages

* Or instead, answer any questions
  your sponsor has recommended

* Use the blank pages at the back if
  you need more space

1) What specific activities have been part of my addictive behaviours and rituals?

2) In what ways have I been pre-occupied with my addiction (e.g. obsessing, sneaking, taking time that should have been spent with family or work)?

Step One

3) How have I not been able to control these behaviours despite promises and attempts to stop?

4) In what ways have I tried to deny, rationalize, explain or justify my addictive behaviours to myself, my family or others?

We admitted we were powerless over our addiction - that our lives had become unmanageable

5) What lies have I told to cover up my addiction?

6) What behaviours am I ashamed of as a result of my addiction?

Step One

7) Have I risked, or had, an arrest for any illegal behaviour? Have I jeopardized my job, position, or reputation because of my addiction?

8) In what ways have I put my physical and mental health at risk because of my addiction?

We admitted we were powerless over our addiction - that our lives had become unmanageable

9) How has my addiction affected the relationships in my life?

10) How has my addiction affected my self-esteem, self-image or self-respect?

11) In what ways have I acted against my morals, values and beliefs as a result of my addiction?

12) What attempts have I made to try and stop or control my addiction? What happened? How successful were they?

We admitted we were powerless over our addiction - that our lives had become unmanageable

66

We perceive that only through utter defeat are we able to take our first steps toward liberation and strength. Our admissions of personal powerlessness finally turn out to be firm bedrock upon which happy and purposeful lives may be built.

Alcoholics Anonymous. (1995). *Twelve Steps and Twelve Traditions*. New York: Alcoholics Anonymous World Services. p.21

66

In recovery, we will be introduced to spiritual principles such as surrender, honesty, and acceptance required for the First Step. If we faithfully practice these principles, they will transform our perceptions and the way we live our lives.

Narcotics Anonymous. (1993). *It Works, How and Why*. Chatsworth, California: Narcotics Anonymous World Services, Inc. p.10-11

"

By honestly looking at what we have become in our addiction, we recognize the powerlessness and unmanageability of our lives. Moving beyond our reservations, we accept our addiction, surrender, and experience the hope that recovery offers. We realize that we can no longer go on as we have been. We are ready for a change. We are willing to try another way.

Narcotics Anonymous. (1993). *It Works, How and Why*. Chatsworth, California: Narcotics Anonymous World Services, Inc. p.16

13) How much money have I spent on my addiction over the years?

14) What areas of my life have become unmanageable? E.g. relationships, friendships, work, health, sexuality, finances

Step One

15) How has my addiction affected my life goals, and my ability to achieve them?

16) How has my addiction affected my health – physical and mental?

We admitted we were powerless over our addiction - that our lives had become unmanageable

17) Who have I harmed as a result of my addiction?

18) How have I used my addiction to change or suppress the way I feel?

19) What about my life became unacceptable to me, and made me enter recovery?

20) List reasons why I should continue in my program of recovery?

We admitted we were powerless over our addiction - that our lives had become unmanageable

21) What are some examples of the ways I have been powerless over my addiction?

Step One

22) What are some examples of how my life has become unmanageable?

24) Am I willing to do whatever it takes to recover?

23) If I continue in my addiction, what will happen?

Step One

Step 1 Completion

I fully concede to my innermost self, that I am powerless over _____ , that my life has become unmanageable.

Signed _____

Date _____

I am now ready for Step 2 ☐

I pray for an open mind so I may come to believe in a Power greater than myself. I pray for humility and the continued opportunity to increase my faith. I don't want to be crazy any more.

Second Step Prayer. Bill P. and Lisa D. *The 12 Step Prayer Book. 2nd ed.* Center City, Minn.: Hazelden, 2004

Step Two

We came to believe that a Power greater than ourselves could restore us to sanity

Guidance

* Use these pages in whichever way serves you best

* Feel free to answer the suggested questions at the side of the pages

* Or instead, answer any questions your sponsor has recommended

* Use the blank pages at the back if you need more space

1) In what ways have I been insane? What insane decisions have I made as a result of my addiction?

2) What does sanity mean to me in the context of my addiction?

3) What changes in my thinking are needed to restore me to sanity?

4) What changes in my behaviour are needed to restore me to sanity?

We came to believe that a Power greater than ourselves could restore us to sanity

5) In what areas of my life do I need sanity?

6) Who do I know who is recovering well? What are they doing that is working?

7) What are some things I consider examples of sanity?

8) In what ways has sanity already been restored to me in my recovery so far?

We came to believe that a Power greater than ourselves could restore us to sanity

9) Have I ever had a spiritual experience? What happened?

10) What are some things that are more powerful than I am?

11) What are the experiences, books, people etc that have shaped my current concept of God or a Higher Power?

12) Why is having a closed mind harmful to my recovery?

We came to believe that a Power greater than ourselves could restore us to sanity

When, therefore, we speak to you of God, we mean your own conception of God. This applies, too, to other spiritual expressions which you find in this book. Do not let any prejudice you may have against spiritual terms deter you from honestly asking yourself what they mean to you. At the start, this was all we needed to commence spiritual growth, to effect our first conscious relation with God as we understood Him.

Alcoholics Anonymous. (2001). *Alcoholics Anonymous, 4th Edition.* New York: A.A. World Services. p.47. (AKA 'The Big Book of AA').

66

When we accept that our way doesn't work, Step Two opens the door to a new way that does. Step Two offers hope that sanity is possible, and at the same time it implies that, in our addiction, we were insane.

Sex Addicts Anonymous. (2014). *Sex Addicts Anonymous, 3rd Edition*. International Service Organization of SAA. p.25

13) What are my negative thoughts, feelings, attitudes or beliefs that block my spirituality?

14) What are my grievances against a Higher Power?

15) What characteristics does my Higher Power NOT have?

16) What characteristics DOES my Higher Power have?

We came to believe that a Power greater than ourselves could restore us to sanity

17) Do I have any fears about coming to believe? What are they?

18) Do I have any other obstacles that make it hard for me to believe? What are they?

19) What is the evidence that a Higher Power is working in my life?

20) How can I seek help from a Power greater than myself today?

We came to believe that a Power greater than ourselves could restore us to sanity

My conception of my Higher Power

....

....

....

....

....

....

....

....

....

....

....

....

....

....

....

....

....

....

....

....

....

....

Step 2 Completion

I have come to believe that a Power greater than myself can restore me to sanity.

Signed _____

Date _____

I am now ready for Step 3 ☐

The Third Step is a turning point. In taking this step, we find the willingness to allow a God of our understanding to work in our lives. Having accepted both the reality of our disease and the possibility that a Higher Power can help us where our own efforts have failed, we make a leap of faith, turning to that Power for assistance. Our understanding of this Power does not need to be perfect or complete in order for us to take this step. We need only an open mind and a willingness to try something new.

Sex Addicts Anonymous. (2014). *Sex Addicts Anonymous, 3rd Edition*. International Service Organization of SAA. p.28

Step Three

We made a decision to turn our will and our lives over to the care of God *as we understood Him*

Guidance

* Use these pages in whichever way serves you best

* Feel free to answer the suggested questions on the side of the pages

* Or instead, answer any questions your sponsor has recommended

* Use the blank pages at the back if you need more space

Step Three

---

1) How have I used my will?

2) When has my will not been enough?

3) When I'm acting on self-will, what typically are my motives?

4) What have been the results, good and bad, of living my life based on self-will?

We made a decision to turn our will and our lives over to the care of God as we understood Him

Step Three

5) How has living based on self-will affected the people in my life?

6) What is the difference between my will and God's will?

7) What does "to the care of" mean to me?

8) What does turning my will and my life over to the care of God mean to me?

We made a decision to turn our will and our lives over to the care of God as we understood Him

66

This is the how and the why of it. First of all, we had to quit playing God. It didn't work. Next, we decided that hereafter in this drama of life, God was going to be our Director. He is the Principal; we are His agents. He is the Father, and we are His children. Most good ideas are simple, and this concept was the keystone of the new and triumphant arch through which we passed to freedom.

Alcoholics Anonymous. (2001). *Alcoholics Anonymous, 4th Edition.* New York: A.A. World Services. p.62. (AKA 'The Big Book of AA').

66

It is when we try to make our will conform with God's that we begin to use it rightly. To all of us, this was a most wonderful revelation. Our whole trouble had been the misuse of willpower. We had tried to bombard our problems with it instead of attempting to bring it into agreement with God's intention for us. To make this increasingly possible is the purpose of [the] Twelve Steps, and Step Three opens the door.

Adapted from: Alcoholics Anonymous. (1995). *Twelve Steps and Twelve Traditions*. New York: Alcoholics Anonymous World Services. p.40.

Step Three

_____

_____

_____

_____

_____

_____

_____

_____

_____

_____

_____

_____

_____

_____

_____

_____

_____

_____

_____

9) What fears do I have about turning my will and my life over to the care of God as I understand Him?

10) What other feelings do I have about turning my will and my life over?

11) Which areas of my life am I most willing to turn over?

12) Which areas of my life are difficult for me to turn over?

We made a decision to turn our will and our lives over to the care of God as we understood Him

Step Three

13) In what ways can my Higher Power help me handle my life better than I have been myself?

14) How might my life change if I turn my will and my life over to the care of my Higher Power?

15) How is my Higher Power working in my life?

16) What things can I do to reinforce my decision to turn my will and my life over?

We made a decision to turn our will and our lives over to the care of God as we understood Him

Step 3 Prayer from the 'The Big Book of AA':

God, I offer myself to Thee—to build with me and to do with me as Thou wilt. Relieve me of the bondage of self, that I may better do Thy will. Take away my difficulties, that victory over them may bear witness to those I would help of Thy Power, Thy Love, and Thy Way of Life. May I do Thy will always!

~

Step 3 Prayer (Dr Bob):

Dear God,

I'm sorry about the mess I've made of my life. I want to turn away from all the wrong things I've ever done and all the wrong things I've ever been. Please forgive me for it all. I know You have the power to change my life and can turn me into a winner. Thank You, God for getting my attention long enough to interest me in trying it Your way. God, please take over the management of my life and everything about me. I am making this conscious decision to turn my will and my life over to Your care and am asking You to please take over all parts of my life. Please, God, move into my heart. However You do it is Your business, but make Yourself real inside me and fill my awful emptiness. Fill me with your love and Holy Spirit and make me know Your will for me. And now, God, help Yourself to me and keep on doing it. I'm not sure I want You to, but do it anyhow. I rejoice that I am now a part of Your people, that my uncertainty is gone forever, and that You now have control of my will and my life. Thank You and I praise Your name.

Amen.

~

An Atheist/Agnostic Step 3 Prayer:

I surrender my life and my will to the Universe, in order to be built into a recovered addict and to be rendered useful to other addicts and to the Universe. I release to the Universe the bondage of self, that I may better understand my purpose and act on it. I release to the Universe my difficulties, so I can live the program and share my story with addicts who still suffer—using the power, the unconditional love, and the recovered life that a personal relationship with an HP provides. I joyfully surrender today, knowing the sanity and serenity a HP-driven life brings.

Step 3 Completion

I have made a decision to turn my will and my life over to the care of God as I understand Him

Signed _____

Date _____

I am now ready for Step 4 ☐

Resentments

Fears

Sex Conduct

Harms

Step Four

We made a searching and fearless moral inventory of ourselves

Guidance

* Use these pages in whichever way serves you best

* Work through each inventory, one by one, using the guidance in the pages ahead

* Use the blank pages at the back if you need more space

* After each inventory, there is a suggested prayer

Step Four

We made a searching and fearless moral inventory of ourselves

> We also clutch at another wonderful excuse for avoiding an inventory. Our present anxieties and troubles, we cry, are caused by the behavior of other people—people who really need a moral inventory. We firmly believe that if only they'd treat us better, we'd be all right. Therefore we think our indignation is justified and reasonable—that our resentments are the "right kind." We aren't the guilty ones. They are!

Alcoholics Anonymous. (1995). *Twelve Steps and Twelve Traditions*. New York: Alcoholics Anonymous World Services. p.45-46.

Resentments Inventory

Father, show me Your will.

Help me see beyond what I think I know
about myself.

Show me Your Truth, Father – the real
Truth about myself.

Guidance

1) On the next page, follow the guidance and list all people, institutions and principles with whom you are angry, resentful, feel hurt or threatened by. Be thorough.

2) One by one, write the person, institution or principle in column 1, and write the cause(s) in column 2. Where there is more than one cause, write each cause in a separate box (see example below). Do this for each person, institution and principle on your list. If you need more space, then you can use the Notes section at the back.

3) Now work your way down column 3. For each resentment, consider how it made you feel and mark which parts of self were affected. The *Useful Definitions* page will be helpful here. Do this for ALL resentments before moving on.

4) Now work your way down column 4. For each resentment, consider where you were to blame. What was your part in it? What did you do initially to get the ball rolling? How could you have done things differently? Do this for ALL resentments before moving on.

5) For each resentment, consider the exact nature of your wrongs and mark them in column 5. The Useful Definitions page will be helpful here. Do this for ALL resentments.

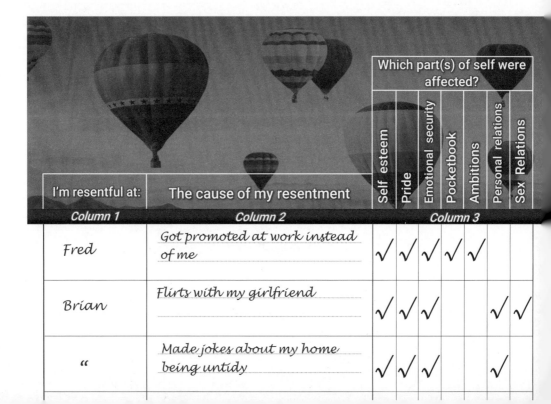

I'm resentful at:	The cause of my resentment	Self esteem	Pride	Emotional security	Pocketbook	Ambitions	Personal relations	Sex Relations
Column 1	Column 2			Column 3				
Fred	Got promoted at work instead of me	✓	✓	✓	✓	✓		
Brian	Flirts with my girlfriend	✓	✓	✓			✓	✓
"	Made jokes about my home being untidy	✓	✓	✓			✓	

Which part(s) of self were affected?

Tips for Success

✦ Be thorough and be specific.

✦ 'Little and often' can be a good strategy for working through step 4 inventories. Get into the habit of writing every day, even if it's just for a few minutes

✦ Work your way down the columns, not across. Complete each column in full before moving on to the next one.

✦ Be honest. The only person to truly benefit from this exercise is you, don't cheat yourself out of this life-changing experience.

✦ If you get stuck or are unsure about anything, call somebody and ask for their experience.

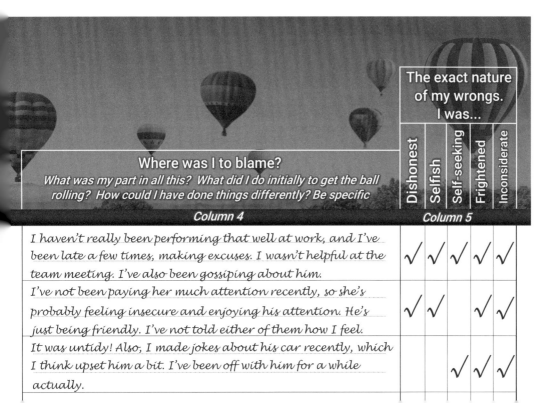

Where was I to blame? What was my part in all this? What did I do initially to get the ball rolling? How could I have done things differently? Be specific	The exact nature of my wrongs. I was...				
Column 4	Dishonest	Selfish	Self-seeking	Frightened	Inconsiderate
			Column 5		
I haven't really been performing that well at work, and I've been late a few times, making excuses. I wasn't helpful at the team meeting. I've also been gossiping about him.	✓	✓	✓	✓	✓
I've not been paying her much attention recently, so she's probably feeling insecure and enjoying his attention. He's just being friendly. I've not told either of them how I feel.	✓	✓		✓	✓
It was untidy! Also, I made jokes about his car recently, which I think upset him a bit. I've been off with him for a while actually.			✓	✓	✓

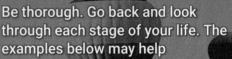

List all people, institutions and principles with whom you are angry, resentful, feel hurt or threatened by

Be thorough. Go back and look through each stage of your life. The examples below may help

People

Parents (step)	In-Laws	Police
Siblings (step)	Children	Doctors
Aunts	Friends	Lawyers
Uncles	School friends	Judges
Cousins	Acquaintances	Probation officers
Grandparents	Co-workers	Creditors / Debtors
Husbands / Wives	Bosses	Teachers
Boyfriends / Girlfriends	People in recovery	Clergy

Institutions

Religion	Authority	Mental health system
Bible	Marriage	Correctional system
Law	Education system	Philosophy
Government	Health system	Military

Principles

God	Heaven	Racism
Jesus	Hell	Homophobia
Satan	Sin	Sexism
Ten Commandments	Adultery	Death

Step Four

My Resentments List

We made a searching and fearless
moral inventory of ourselves

> " It is plain that a life which includes deep resentment leads only to futility and unhappiness. To the precise extent that we permit these, do we squander the hours that might have been worth while. But with the alcoholic [addict], whose hope is the maintenance and growth of a spiritual experience, this business of resentment is infinitely grave. We found that it is fatal. For when harboring such feelings we shut ourselves off from the sunlight of the Spirit.

Alcoholics Anonymous. (2001). *Alcoholics Anonymous, 4th Edition*. New York: A.A. World Services. p.66. (AKA 'The Big Book of AA').

Useful Definitions

Resentment	Feelings of bitterness, hurt or indignation which come from rightly or wrongly held feelings of being injured or offended
Self esteem	How I think of myself
Pride	How I think others view me
Emotional security	General sense of personal wellbeing
Pocketbook	Basic desire for money, possessions, property
Ambitions	Our goals, plans and designs for the future
Personal relations	Our relations with other people
Sex relations	Basic drive for sexual intimacy
Dishonest	The act or practice of telling a lie, cheating, deceiving or stealing
Selfish	Concerned with one's own welfare or interests and having little or no concern for others
Self-seeking	Seeking or pursuing only for oneself / the act or practice of selfishly advancing one's own desires and goals
Frightened	A temporary of continual state of fear or anxiety
Inconsiderate	Without thought or consideration for others

Resentments

I'm resentful at:	The cause of my resentment	Self esteem	Pride	Emotional security	Pocketbook	Ambitions	Personal relations	Sex relations
Column 1	Column 2				Column 3			

Which part(s) of self were affected?

Step Four

Where was I to blame? What was my part in all this? What did I do initially to get the ball rolling? How could I have done things differently? Be specific	The exact nature of my wrongs. I was...				
Column 4	Dishonest	Selfish	Self-seeking	Frightened	Inconsiderate

We made a searching and fearless moral inventory of ourselves

Resentments

I'm resentful at:	The cause of my resentment	Self esteem	Pride	Emotional security	Pocketbook	Ambitions	Personal relations	Sex relations
Column 1	Column 2	Column 3						

Which part(s) of self were affected?

Step Four

Where was I to blame? What was my part in all this? What did I do initially to get the ball rolling? How could I have done things differently? Be specific	The exact nature of my wrongs. I was...				
	Dishonest	Selfish	Self-seeking	Frightened	Inconsiderate
Column 4	Column 5				

We made a searching and fearless moral inventory of ourselves

Resentments

I'm resentful at:	The cause of my resentment	Which part(s) of self were affected?						
Column 1	Column 2	Self esteem	Pride	Emotional security	Pocketbook	Ambitions	Personal relations	Sex relations

Step Four

Where was I to blame? What was my part in all this? What did I do initially to get the ball rolling? How could I have done things differently? Be specific	The exact nature of my wrongs. I was...				
Column 4	Dishonest	Selfish	Self-seeking	Frightened	Inconsiderate

We made a searching and fearless moral inventory of ourselves

Resentments

I'm resentful at:	The cause of my resentment	Self esteem	Pride	Emotional security	Pocketbook	Ambitions	Personal relations	Sex relations
Column 1	Column 2				Column 3			

Which part(s) of self were affected?

Step Four

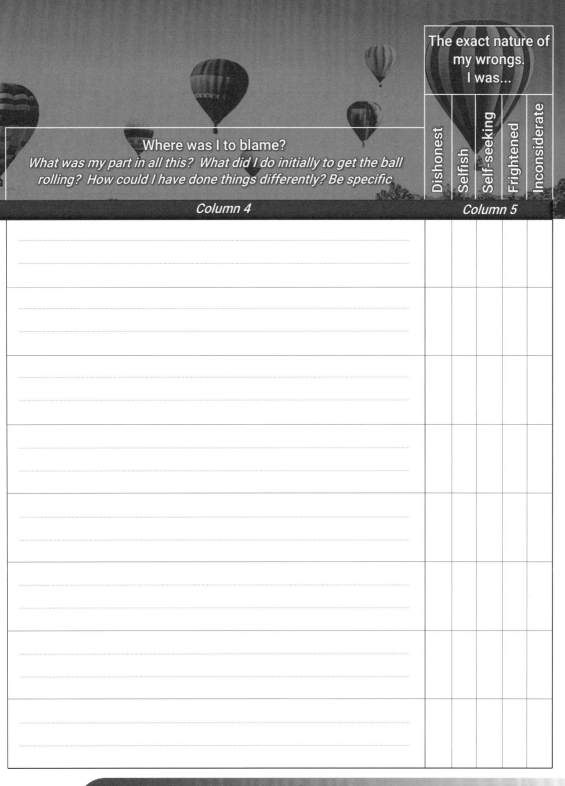

Where was I to blame? What was my part in all this? What did I do initially to get the ball rolling? How could I have done things differently? Be specific	The exact nature of my wrongs. I was...				
Column 4	Dishonest	Selfish	Self-seeking	Frightened	Inconsiderate
	Column 5				

We made a searching and fearless moral inventory of ourselves

Resentments

I'm resentful at:	The cause of my resentment	Self esteem	Pride	Emotional security	Pocketbook	Ambitions	Personal relations	Sex relations
Column 1	**Column 2**				**Column 3**			

Which part(s) of self were affected?

Step Four

Where was I to blame? What was my part in all this? What did I do initially to get the ball rolling? How could I have done things differently? Be specific	The exact nature of my wrongs. I was...				
Column 4	Dishonest	Selfish	Self-seeking	Frightened	Inconsiderate
	Column 5				

We made a searching and fearless
moral inventory of ourselves

Resentments

I'm resentful at:	The cause of my resentment	Self esteem	Pride	Emotional security	Pocketbook	Ambitions	Personal relations	Sex relations
Column 1	Column 2	Column 3						

Which part(s) of self were affected?

Step Four

Where was I to blame? What was my part in all this? What did I do initially to get the ball rolling? How could I have done things differently? Be specific	The exact nature of my wrongs. I was...				
Column 4	Dishonest	Selfish	Self-seeking	Frightened	Inconsiderate

We made a searching and fearless moral inventory of ourselves

Resentments

I'm resentful at:	The cause of my resentment	Which part(s) of self were affected?						
		Self esteem	Pride	Emotional security	Pocketbook	Ambitions	Personal relations	Sex relations
Column 1	Column 2	Column 3						

Step Four

Where was I to blame? What was my part in all this? What did I do initially to get the ball rolling? How could I have done things differently? Be specific	The exact nature of my wrongs. I was...				
Column 4	Dishonest	Selfish	Self-seeking	Frightened	Inconsiderate

We made a searching and fearless moral inventory of ourselves

Resentments

I'm resentful at:	The cause of my resentment	Self esteem	Pride	Emotional security	Pocketbook	Ambitions	Personal relations	Sex relations
Column 1	Column 2				Column 3			

Which part(s) of self were affected?

Step Four

Where was I to blame? What was my part in all this? What did I do initially to get the ball rolling? How could I have done things differently? Be specific	The exact nature of my wrongs. I was...				
Column 4	Column 5				
	Dishonest	Selfish	Self-seeking	Frightened	Inconsiderate

We made a searching and fearless moral inventory of ourselves

Resentments

I'm resentful at:	The cause of my resentment	Which part(s) of self were affected?						
		Self esteem	Pride	Emotional security	Pocketbook	Ambitions	Personal relations	Sex relations
Column 1	Column 2	Column 3						

Step Four

Where was I to blame? What was my part in all this? What did I do initially to get the ball rolling? How could I have done things differently? Be specific	The exact nature of my wrongs. I was...				
Column 4	Dishonest	Selfish	Self-seeking	Frightened	Inconsiderate

We made a searching and fearless moral inventory of ourselves

Resentments

I'm resentful at:	The cause of my resentment	Self esteem	Pride	Emotional security	Pocketbook	Ambitions	Personal relations	Sex relations
Column 1	Column 2				Column 3			

Which part(s) of self were affected?

Step Four

Where was I to blame? What was my part in all this? What did I do initially to get the ball rolling? How could I have done things differently? Be specific	The exact nature of my wrongs. I was...				
Column 4	Dishonest	Selfish	Self-seeking	Frightened	Inconsiderate

We made a searching and fearless moral inventory of ourselves

God please help me show _____ the same tolerance, pity, and patience that I would cheerfully grant a sick friend. Help me to see that, this is perhaps a spiritually sick person too. Show me how I can be helpful to them. God save me from being angry.

Lord help me to avoid retaliation or argument. I know I cannot be helpful to all people, but at least show me how to take a kindly and tolerant view of each and every one. Thy will be done.

Adapted from : Alcoholics Anonymous. (2001). *Alcoholics Anonymous, 4th Edition*. New York: A.A. World Services. p.67. (AKA 'The Big Book of AA').

> *We reviewed our fears thoroughly. We put them on paper, even though we had no resentment in connection with them. We asked ourselves why we had them. Wasn't it because self-reliance failed us? Self-reliance was good as far as it went, but it didn't go far enough. Some of us once had great self-confidence, but it didn't fully solve the fear problem, or any other.*

Alcoholics Anonymous. (2001). *Alcoholics Anonymous, 4th Edition.* New York: A.A. World Services. p.68. (AKA 'The Big Book of AA').

Step Four

We made a searching and fearless moral inventory of ourselves

God, please give me Your
patience, tolerance, faith,
strength, and courage I
need to do this work.

Remove my fears of what
I may find out about
myself.

Help me God...Help me to
see and experience the
Truth about myself.

Fears Inventory

1) In column 1, list all of your fears. The examples on the next page may help. Be thorough and be specific. Look back through your life in detail. Complete all of column 1 before moving on.

2) In column 2, consider why you think you have each of your fears. Where did they originate from? And think about how each one has impacted or harmed you, or others in your life. Complete column 2 before moving on.

3) For each fear, consider which part(s) of self you have been relying on, which has let you down. Mark them in column 3. If you get stuck, call someone and ask for their experience. Complete column 3 before moving on.

4) Next, think about which part(s) of self each fear affects, and mark them in column 4. Complete column 4 before moving on.

5) Now, work down column 5, and for each fear, write what was your role in it? What actions and decisions did you take? How did you get the ball rolling that led to a chain of events which left you in a position to have this fear? Be specific. Complete column 5 before moving on.

6) Finally, for each fear, consider which character defects have played a role in either your actions, or to you wanting to hold on to the fear. Mark them in column 6.

Examples of Fears

Failure   Authority   Dying   Loneliness   Religion

Losing a loved one   Not being in control   Not having enough sex

Men   Change   Government   Heights   Women

Not having a job   Public speaking   Animals   Relationships

Hospitals   Parents   Love   Success   LGBT people

Physical pain   Other races   Getting a job   Mental illness

Not being in a relationship   Hurting others   Not having enough money

Police   Diseases   Water   Intimacy   Creditors

Being alone   Having children   Self-expression   Commitment

Abandonment   Confrontation   Anger   Disapproval   God

Feelings   Fear itself   Violence   Alcohol   Gangs

Not having children   The unknown   Responsibility   What people think

Rejection   People   Sex   Doctors   Guns

Getting old   Being found out   Sobriety

Insects   Drugs   Jail   Dentist

Relapse   Sin   Crying   Lies

We made a searching and fearless
moral inventory of ourselves

Fears

The fear	Why do I have this fear? What impacts or harms has this fear had on me and others?	Which part(s) of self have I been relying on which have failed me?			
		Self-reliance	Self-confidence	Self-discipline	Self-will
Column 1	Column 2	Column 3			

Step Four

Which part(s) of self does the fear affect?							What was MY part in this? What did I do to get the ball rolling that led to my being in the position to have the fear?	Which character defects contributed to my actions or to me holding on to the old fear?				
Self esteem	Pride	Emotional security	Pocketbook	Ambitions	Personal relations	Sex relations		Dishonest	Selfish	Self-seeking	Frightened	Inconsiderate
Column 4							Column 5	Column 6				

We made a searching and fearless
moral inventory of ourselves

Fears

The fear	Why do I have this fear? What impacts or harms has this fear had on me and others?	Which part(s) of self have I been relying on which have failed me?			
		Self-reliance	Self-confidence	Self-discipline	Self-will
Column 1	*Column 2*	*Column 3*			

Step Four

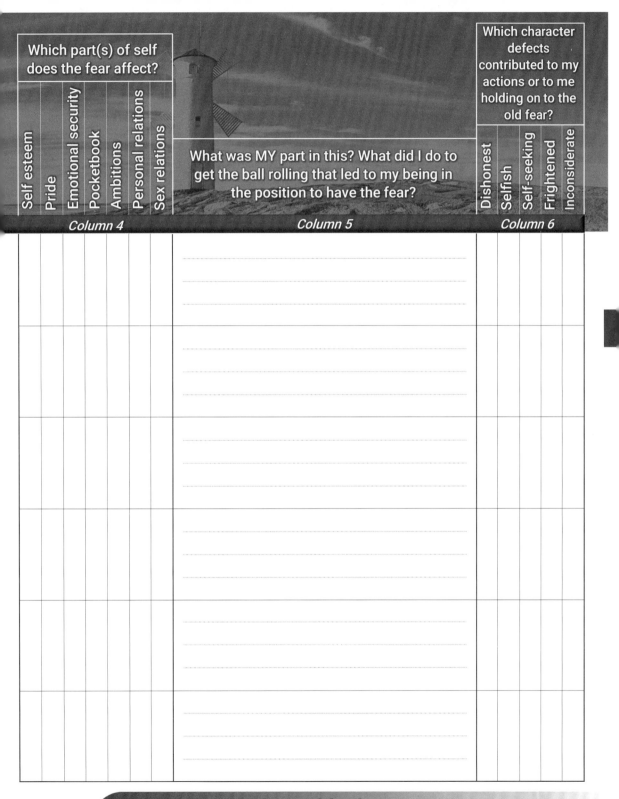

Which part(s) of self does the fear affect?							What was MY part in this? What did I do to get the ball rolling that led to my being in the position to have the fear?	Which character defects contributed to my actions or to me holding on to the old fear?				
Self esteem	Pride	Emotional security	Pocketbook	Ambitions	Personal relations	Sex relations		Dishonest	Selfish	Self-seeking	Frightened	Inconsiderate
Column 4							_Column 5_	_Column 6_				

We made a searching and fearless moral inventory of ourselves

The fear	Why do I have this fear? What impacts or harms has this fear had on me and others?	Self-reliance	Self-confidence	Self-discipline	Self-will
Column 1	Column 2	Column 3			

Fears

Which part(s) of self have I been relying on which have failed me?

Step Four

Which part(s) of self does the fear affect?							What was MY part in this? What did I do to get the ball rolling that led to my being in the position to have the fear?	Which character defects contributed to my actions or to me holding on to the old fear?				
Self esteem	Pride	Emotional security	Pocketbook	Ambitions	Personal relations	Sex relations		Dishonest	Selfish	Self-seeking	Frightened	Inconsiderate
Column 4							Column 5	Column 6				

We made a searching and fearless
moral inventory of ourselves

Fears

The fear	Why do I have this fear? What impacts or harms has this fear had on me and others?	Which part(s) of self have I been relying on which have failed me?			
		Self-reliance	Self-confidence	Self-discipline	Self-will
Column 1	Column 2	Column 3			

Step Four

Which part(s) of self does the fear affect?							What was MY part in this? What did I do to get the ball rolling that led to my being in the position to have the fear?	Which character defects contributed to my actions or to me holding on to the old fear?				
Self esteem	Pride	Emotional security	Pocketbook	Ambitions	Personal relations	Sex relations		Dishonest	Selfish	Self-seeking	Frightened	Inconsiderate
Column 4							*Column 5*	*Column 6*				

We made a searching and fearless moral inventory of ourselves

Fears	Why do I have this fear? What impacts or harms has this fear had on me and others?	Which part(s) of self have I been relying on which have failed me?			
The fear		Self-reliance	Self-confidence	Self-discipline	Self-will
Column 1	Column 2	Column 3			

Step Four

Which part(s) of self does the fear affect?							What was MY part in this? What did I do to get the ball rolling that led to my being in the position to have the fear?	Which character defects contributed to my actions or to me holding on to the old fear?				
Self esteem	Pride	Emotional security	Pocketbook	Ambitions	Personal relations	Sex relations		Dishonest	Selfish	Self-seeking	Frightened	Inconsiderate
Column 4							Column 5	Column 6				

We made a searching and fearless moral inventory of ourselves

Fears

The fear	Why do I have this fear? What impacts or harms has this fear had on me and others?	Which part(s) of self have I been relying on which have failed me?			
		Self-reliance	Self-confidence	Self-discipline	Self-will
Column 1	Column 2	Column 3			

Step Four

Which part(s) of self does the fear affect?							What was MY part in this? What did I do to get the ball rolling that led to my being in the position to have the fear?	Which character defects contributed to my actions or to me holding on to the old fear?				
Self esteem	Pride	Emotional security	Pocketbook	Ambitions	Personal relations	Sex relations		Dishonest	Selfish	Self-seeking	Frightened	Inconsiderate
Column 4							Column 5	Column 6				

We made a searching and fearless moral inventory of ourselves

Fears

The fear	Why do I have this fear? What impacts or harms has this fear had on me and others?	Which part(s) of self have I been relying on which have failed me?			
		Self-reliance	Self-confidence	Self-discipline	Self-will
Column 1	Column 2	Column 3			

Step Four

Which part(s) of self does the fear affect?							What was MY part in this? What did I do to get the ball rolling that led to my being in the position to have the fear?	Which character defects contributed to my actions or to me holding on to the old fear?				
Self esteem	Pride	Emotional security	Pocketbook	Ambitions	Personal relations	Sex relations		Dishonest	Selfish	Self-seeking	Frightened	Inconsiderate
Column 4							*Column 5*	*Column 6*				

We made a searching and fearless moral inventory of ourselves

Fears

The fear	Why do I have this fear? What impacts or harms has this fear had on me and others?	Which part(s) of self have I been relying on which have failed me?			
		Self-reliance	Self-confidence	Self-discipline	Self-will
Column 1	Column 2	Column 3			

Step Four

Which part(s) of self does the fear affect?							What was MY part in this? What did I do to get the ball rolling that led to my being in the position to have the fear?	Which character defects contributed to my actions or to me holding on to the old fear?				
Self esteem	Pride	Emotional security	Pocketbook	Ambitions	Personal relations	Sex relations		Dishonest	Selfish	Self-seeking	Frightened	Inconsiderate
Column 4							*Column 5*	*Column 6*				

We made a searching and fearless moral inventory of ourselves

God, thank You for helping me to be honest enough to see the truth about myself.

Thank You for showing me my fears, please help me remove them.

Help me outgrow my fears;

The fears that have haunted me and blocked me from doing Your will.

Direct my attention to what You would have me be.

The Fear Prayer. Bill P. and Lisa D. *The 12 Step Prayer Book. 2nd ed.* Center City, Minn.: Hazelden, 2004

Step Four

We made a searching and fearless
moral inventory of ourselves

> *Now about sex. Many of us needed an overhauling
> there. But above all, we tried to be sensible on this
> question. It's so easy to get way off the track.*

Alcoholics Anonymous. (2001). *Alcoholics Anonymous, 4th Edition*. New
York: A.A. World Services. p.68. (AKA 'The Big Book of AA').

Sex Conduct Inventory

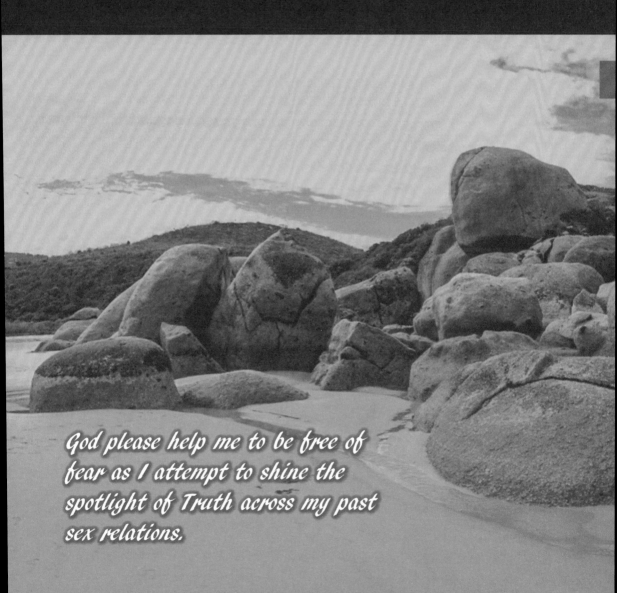

God please help me to be free of fear as I attempt to shine the spotlight of Truth across my past sex relations.

> 66
>
> *We all have sex problems. We'd hardly be human if we didn't. What can we do about them?*
>
> *We reviewed our own conduct over the years past. Where had we been selfish, dishonest, or inconsiderate? Whom had we hurt? Did we unjustifiably arouse jealousy, suspicion or bitterness? Where were we at fault, what should we have done instead? We got this all down on paper and looked at it.*

Alcoholics Anonymous. (2001). *Alcoholics Anonymous, 4th Edition.* New York: A.A. World Services. p.69. (AKA 'The Big Book of AA').

Guidance

1) In column 1, list all the people you've harmed through your sexual conduct throughout your entire life. Be thorough. Complete column 1 before moving on.

2) In column 2, write what you did to cause harm or hurt to the person. Be specific. If you suffered guilt or shame as a result of your conduct, write this too. Complete column 2 before moving on.

3) Next, consider if you were selfish, dishonest or inconsiderate, and mark them in column 3. Complete column 3 before moving on.

4) Now, reflect on if you unjustifiably caused jealousy, suspicion or bitterness and mark them in column 4. Complete column 4 before moving on.

5) In column 5, write the specifics of where you were at fault – the exact nature of your wrongs. How were you selfish, self-seeking, dishonest, fearful, inconsiderate or uncaring? Complete column 5 before moving on.

6) Finally, in column 6, consider what you should have done instead. For example, should you have shown respect, been a friend, been open and honest, treated them as you would've wanted to be treated, not used them, or shown care.

Sex Conduct

Who did I harm?	What did I do?	I was...			I aroused...		
		Selfish	Dishonest	Inconsiderate	Jealousy	Suspicion	Bitterness
Column 1	Column 2	Column 3			Column 4		

Step Four

Where was I at fault? Was I selfish, self-seeking, dishonest, fearful, inconsiderate, uncaring?	What should I have done instead? E.g. shown respect, been a friend, been open and honest, treated them as I would've wanted to be treated, not used them, shown care
Column 5	Column 6

We made a searching and fearless
moral inventory of ourselves

Sex Conduct

Who did I harm?	What did I do?	I was...			I aroused...		
		Selfish	Dishonest	Inconsiderate	Jealousy	Suspicion	Bitterness
Column 1	Column 2	Column 3			Column 4		

Step Four

Where was I at fault? Was I selfish, self-seeking, dishonest, fearful, inconsiderate, uncaring?	What should I have done instead? E.g. shown respect, been a friend, been open and honest, treated them as I would've wanted to be treated, not used them, shown care
Column 5	Column 6

We made a searching and fearless moral inventory of ourselves

Sex Conduct

Who did I harm?	What did I do?	I was...			I aroused...		
		Selfish	Dishonest	Inconsiderate	Jealousy	Suspicion	Bitterness
Column 1	Column 2	Column 3			Column 4		

Step Four

Where was I at fault? Was I selfish, self-seeking, dishonest, fearful, inconsiderate, uncaring?	What should I have done instead? E.g. shown respect, been a friend, been open and honest, treated them as I would've wanted to be treated, not used them, shown care
Column 5	Column 6

We made a searching and fearless moral inventory of ourselves

Sex Conduct

Who did I harm?	What did I do?	I was...			I aroused...		
		Selfish	Dishonest	Inconsiderate	Jealousy	Suspicion	Bitterness
Column 1	Column 2	Column 3			Column 4		

Step Four

Where was I at fault? *Was I selfish, self-seeking, dishonest, fearful, inconsiderate, uncaring?*	What should I have done instead? *E.g. shown respect, been a friend, been open and honest, treated them as I would've wanted to be treated, not used them, shown care*
Column 5	Column 6

We made a searching and fearless
moral inventory of ourselves

Sex Conduct

Who did I harm?	What did I do?	I was...			I aroused...		
		Selfish	Dishonest	Inconsiderate	Jealousy	Suspicion	Bitterness
Column 1	Column 2	Column 3			Column 4		

Step Four

Where was I at fault? *Was I selfish, self-seeking, dishonest, fearful, inconsiderate, uncaring?*	What should I have done instead? *E.g. shown respect, been a friend, been open and honest, treated them as I would've wanted to be treated, not used them, shown care*
Column 5	Column 6

We made a searching and fearless
moral inventory of ourselves

Sex Conduct

Who did I harm?	What did I do?	I was...			I aroused...		
		Selfish	Dishonest	Inconsiderate	Jealousy	Suspicion	Bitterness
Column 1	Column 2	Column 3			Column 4		

Step Four

Where was I at fault? *Was I selfish, self-seeking, dishonest, fearful, inconsiderate, uncaring?*	What should I have done instead? *E.g. shown respect, been a friend, been open and honest, treated them as I would've wanted to be treated, not used them, shown care*
Column 5	Column 6

We made a searching and fearless moral inventory of ourselves

Sex Conduct

Who did I harm?	What did I do?	I was...			I aroused...		
		Selfish	Dishonest	Inconsiderate	Jealousy	Suspicion	Bitterness
Column 1	Column 2	Column 3			Column 4		

Step Four

Where was I at fault? Was I selfish, self-seeking, dishonest, fearful, inconsiderate, uncaring?	What should I have done instead? E.g. shown respect, been a friend, been open and honest, treated them as I would've wanted to be treated, not used them, shown care
Column 5	Column 6

We made a searching and fearless
moral inventory of ourselves

Sex Conduct

Who did I harm?	What did I do?	I was...			I aroused...		
		Selfish	Dishonest	Inconsiderate	Jealousy	Suspicion	Bitterness
Column 1	Column 2	Column 3			Column 4		

Step Four

Where was I at fault? Was I selfish, self-seeking, dishonest, fearful, inconsiderate, uncaring?	What should I have done instead? E.g. shown respect, been a friend, been open and honest, treated them as I would've wanted to be treated, not used them, shown care
Column 5	Column 6

We made a searching and fearless moral inventory of ourselves

God, please mold my sex ideals and help me live up to them. Lord, help me find the right sex ideal for myself, and please guide me in each questionable sex situation.

My sex powers were given to me by You, and therefore they are good, neither to be used lightly or selfishly, nor to be despised or loathed.

Please tell me what I can do in each specific matter. I trust You will give me the right answer when I truly want it.

Adapted from : Alcoholics Anonymous. (2001). *Alcoholics Anonymous, 4th Edition*. New York: A.A. World Services. p.69. (AKA 'The Big Book of AA').

" We have listed the people we have hurt by our conduct, and are willing to straighten out the past if we can.

Alcoholics Anonymous. (2001). *Alcoholics Anonymous, 4th Edition*. New York: A.A. World Services. p.70. (AKA 'The Big Book of AA').

Step Four

We made a searching and fearless
moral inventory of ourselves

Lord, please show me where my behavior has harmed others and help me to see the Truth these relationships hold for me.
Help me see where I have been at fault and what I should have done differently

Harms Inventory

> When we habitually tried to manipulate others to our own willful desires, they revolt, and resist us heavily. Then we develop hurt feelings, a sense of persecution, and a desire to retaliate. As we redouble our efforts at control, and continue to fail, our suffering becomes acute and constant. We have not once sought to be one in a family, to be a friend among friends, to be a worker among workers, to be a useful member of society. Always we tried to struggle to the top of the heap, or to hide underneath it. This self-centered behavior blocked a partnership relation with any one of those about us. Of true brotherhood we had small comprehension.

Alcoholics Anonymous. (1995). *Twelve Steps and Twelve Traditions*. New York: Alcoholics Anonymous World Services. p.53

Guidance

1) In column 1, list all the people and institutions you've harmed. Review your entire life and be thorough, list them all. Complete column 1 before moving on.

2) In column 2, write what you did, or failed to do, that caused the harm. Be specific. Complete column 2 before moving on.

3) Next, consider which part(s) of self contributed to the harm, and mark them in column 3. Complete column 3 before moving on.

4) In column 4, reflect on the feelings you created in others as a result of your actions or inactions. Complete column 4 before moving on.

5) Now, consider the exact nature of your wrongs. Were you dishonest, selfish, self-seeking, frightened and/or inconsiderate? Mark them in column 5. Complete column 5 before moving on.

6) Finally, think about what you should have done instead, so as not to have caused the harm. How would your Higher Power have you be instead? What could you do differently next time?

Harms

Who did I harm? *People, institutions* Column 1	What did I do or fail to do to cause the harm? Column 2	Which part(s) of self caused the harm?						
		Self esteem	Pride	Emotional security	Pocketbook	Ambitions	Personal relations	Sex relations

Step Four

What feelings did I create in others? E.g. anger, fear, stress, sadness, shock, loneliness, jealousy	The exact nature of my wrongs. I was...					What should I have done instead? How would my Higher Power have me be instead? What can I do differently next time?
	Dishonest	Selfish	Self-seeking	Frightened	Inconsiderate	
Column 4	Column 5					Column 6

We made a searching and fearless moral inventory of ourselves

Harms

Who did I harm? *People, institutions*	What did I do or fail to do to cause the harm?	Self esteem	Pride	Emotional security	Pocketbook	Ambitions	Personal relations	Sex relations
Column 1	*Column 2*				*Column 3*			

Which part(s) of self caused the harm?

Step Four

What feelings did I create in others? E.g. anger, fear, stress, sadness, shock, loneliness, jealousy Column 4	The exact nature of my wrongs. I was...					What should I have done instead? How would my Higher Power have me be instead? What can I do differently next time? Column 6
	Dishonest	Selfish	Self-seeking	Frightened	Inconsiderate	

We made a searching and fearless moral inventory of ourselves

Harms

Who did I harm? *People, institutions*	What did I do or fail to do to cause the harm?	Self esteem	Pride	Emotional security	Pocketbook	Ambitions	Personal relations	Sex relations
Column 1	Column 2				Column 3			

Which part(s) of self caused the harm?

Step Four

What feelings did I create in others? E.g. anger, fear, stress, sadness, shock, loneliness, jealousy	The exact nature of my wrongs. I was...					What should I have done instead? How would my Higher Power have me be instead? What can I do differently next time?
	Dishonest	Selfish	Self-seeking	Frightened	Inconsiderate	
Column 4	Column 5					Column 6

We made a searching and fearless moral inventory of ourselves

Harms

Who did I harm? _People, institutions_	What did I do or fail to do to cause the harm?	Self esteem	Pride	Emotional security	Pocketbook	Ambitions	Personal relations	Sex relations
Column 1	Column 2				Column 3			

Which part(s) of self caused the harm?

Step Four

What feelings did I create in others? E.g. anger, fear, stress, sadness, shock, loneliness, jealousy	The exact nature of my wrongs. I was...					What should I have done instead? How would my Higher Power have me be instead? What can I do differently next time?
	Dishonest	Selfish	Self-seeking	Frightened	Inconsiderate	
Column 4	Column 5					Column 6

We made a searching and fearless moral inventory of ourselves

Harms

Who did I harm? *People, institutions* Column 1	What did I do or fail to do to cause the harm? Column 2	Which part(s) of self caused the harm?						
		Self esteem	Pride	Emotional security	Pocketbook	Ambitions	Personal relations	Sex relations
	Column 3							

Step Four

What feelings did I create in others? E.g. anger, fear, stress, sadness, shock, loneliness, jealousy	The exact nature of my wrongs. I was...					What should I have done instead? How would my Higher Power have me be instead? What can I do differently next time?
	Dishonest	Selfish	Self-seeking	Frightened	Inconsiderate	
Column 4	Column 5					Column 6

We made a searching and fearless moral inventory of ourselves

Harms

Who did I harm? People, institutions	What did I do or fail to do to cause the harm?	Which part(s) of self caused the harm?						
		Self esteem	Pride	Emotional security	Pocketbook	Ambitions	Personal relations	Sex relations
Column 1	Column 2	Column 3						

Step Four

What feelings did I create in others? E.g. anger, fear, stress, sadness, shock, loneliness, jealousy Column 4	The exact nature of my wrongs. I was...					What should I have done instead? How would my Higher Power have me be instead? What can I do differently next time? Column 6
	Dishonest	Selfish	Self-seeking	Frightened	Inconsiderate	

We made a searching and fearless moral inventory of ourselves

Harms

Who did I harm? *People, institutions*	What did I do or fail to do to cause the harm?	Self esteem	Pride	Emotional security	Pocketbook	Ambitions	Personal relations	Sex relations
Column 1	Column 2				Column 3			

Which part(s) of self caused the harm?

Step Four

What feelings did I create in others? E.g. anger, fear, stress, sadness, shock, loneliness, jealousy	The exact nature of my wrongs. I was...					What should I have done instead? How would my Higher Power have me be instead? What can I do differently next time?
	Dishonest	Selfish	Self-seeking	Frightened	Inconsiderate	
Column 4	Column 5					Column 6

We made a searching and fearless moral inventory of ourselves

Harms

Who did I harm? *People, institutions* Column 1	What did I do or fail to do to cause the harm? Column 2	Which part(s) of self caused the harm? Column 3						
		Self esteem	Pride	Emotional security	Pocketbook	Ambitions	Personal relations	Sex relations

Step Four

What feelings did I create in others? E.g. anger, fear, stress, sadness, shock, loneliness, jealousy	The exact nature of my wrongs. I was...					What should I have done instead? How would my Higher Power have me be instead? What can I do differently next time?
	Dishonest	Selfish	Self-seeking	Frightened	Inconsiderate	
Column 4	Column 5					Column 6

We made a searching and fearless
moral inventory of ourselves

66 *If we have been thorough about our personal inventory, we have written down a lot. We have listed and analyzed our resentments. We have begun to comprehend their futility and their fatality. We have commenced to see their terrible destructiveness. We have begun to learn tolerance, patience and good will toward all men, even our enemies, for we look on them as sick people. We have listed the people we have hurt by our conduct, and are willing to straighten out the past if we can.*

Alcoholics Anonymous. (2001). *Alcoholics Anonymous, 4th Edition*. New York: A.A. World Services. p.70. (AKA 'The Big Book of AA')

Step 4 Completion

I have made a searching
and fearless moral inventory
of myself.

Signed _____

Date _____

I am now ready for Step 5 ☐

Higher Power, my inventory has shown me who I am, yet I ask for Your help in admitting my wrongs to another person and to You. Assure me, and be with me in this Step, for without this Step I cannot progress in my recovery. With Your help, I can do this, and I will do it.

Fifth Step Prayer. Bill P. and Lisa D. *The 12 Step Prayer Book. 2nd ed*. Center City, Minn.: Hazelden, 2004

Step Five

We admitted to God, to ourselves, and to another human being the exact nature of our wrongs

Guidance

* Use these pages in whichever way serves you best

* Feel free to answer the suggested questions on the left of the pages

* Or instead, answer any questions your sponsor has recommended

* Use the blank pages at the back if you need more space

1) What's the difference between my actions and the *exact nature of my wrongs?*

2) How will practicing honesty in this step help me in my recovery and in my life?

3) How will self-acceptance help me in my recovery and in my life?

4) Who have I chosen to hear my Step 5? Why have I chosen this person? What qualities do they have that made me choose them?

We admitted to God, to ourselves, and to another human being, the exact nature of our wrongs

5) Is there anything in my Step 4 inventories that I've missed out because of fear of having to admit it? Can I find the courage necessary to admit it now?

6) How will I include my Higher Power in my Step 5?

7) How have the first four steps helped prepare me for Step 5?

8) Why is it important that I seek out the flaws in my character?

We admitted to God, to ourselves, and to another human being, the exact nature of our wrongs

"

The Fifth Step is the key to freedom. It allows us to live clean in the here and now. Sharing the exact nature of our wrongs sets us free to live. After taking a thorough Fourth Step, we have to deal with what we have found in our inventory. We are told that if we keep these defects inside us, they will lead us back to using. Holding on to our past would eventually sicken us and keep us from taking part in this new way of life. If we are not honest when we take a Fifth Step, we will have the same negative results that dishonesty brought us in the past.

Narcotics Anonymous. (2008). *Narcotics Anonymous: 6th Edition Basic Text*. Chatsworth, California: NA World Services, Inc. p.31

All of [the] Twelve Steps ask us to go contrary to our natural desires... they all deflate our egos. When it comes to ego deflation, few Steps are harder to take than Five. But scarcely any Step is more necessary to longtime sobriety and peace of mind than this one.

Adapted from: Alcoholics Anonymous. (1995). *Twelve Steps and Twelve Traditions*. New York: Alcoholics Anonymous World Services. p.55

9) What fears do I have about admitting the exact nature of my wrongs to God, myself and to another human being?

10) What other feelings do I have about this step?

11) What are my expectations for sharing my Step 4 inventories and the exact nature of my wrongs?

12) How do I think this step will help me and my recovery?

We admitted to God, to ourselves, and to another human being, the exact nature of our wrongs

Step Five

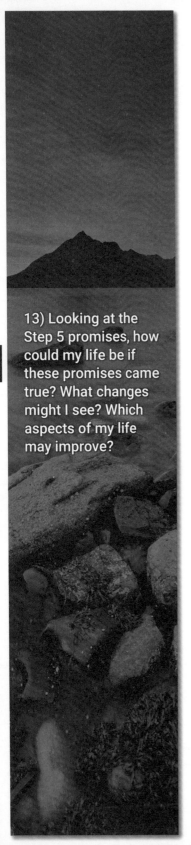

Step 5 Promises

Once we have taken this step, withholding nothing, we are delighted. We can look the world in the eye. We can be alone at perfect peace and ease. Our fears fall from us. We begin to feel the nearness of our Creator. We may have had certain spiritual beliefs, but now we begin to have a spiritual experience. The feeling that [our addiction] problem has disappeared will often come strongly. We feel we are on the Broad Highway, walking hand in hand with the Spirit of the Universe.

Adapted from: Alcoholics Anonymous. (2001). *Alcoholics Anonymous, 4th Edition*. New York: A.A. World Services. p.75. (AKA 'The Big Book of AA').

13) Looking at the Step 5 promises, how could my life be if these promises came true? What changes might I see? Which aspects of my life may improve?

We admitted to God, to ourselves, and to another human being, the exact nature of our wrongs

Step 5 Completion

I have admitted to God, to myself, and to another human being, the exact nature of my wrongs.

Signed _____

Date _____

I am now ready for Step 6 ☐

Step Six

We were entirely ready to have God remove all these defects of character

Dear God,

I am ready for Your help in removing from me the defects of character which I now realize are obstacles to my recovery. Help me to continue being honest with myself and guide me toward spiritual and mental health.

Sixth Step Prayer. Bill P. and Lisa D. *The 12 Step Prayer Book. 2nd ed.* Center City, Minn.: Hazelden, 2004

* Use these pages in whichever way serves you best

* Feel free to answer the suggested questions at the bottom of the pages

* Or instead, answer any questions your sponsor has recommended

* Use the blank pages at the back if you need more space

Thoughtful
Forgiving
Agreeable
Sensitive
Bold
Selfless
Nice
Optimistic
Generous
Organized Disciplined
Kind
Approving
Gentle
Cheerful Good-listener
Honest
Cooperative Relaxed
Controlled
Attentive Helpful
Tolerant Careful Willing
Fun
Patient Flexible Content
Romantic Involved Realistic
Polite Trusting Considerate
Humble Outgoing Witty
Steady Decisive
Giving Assertive Friendly
Open Loving Confident
Analytical Warm
Lawful
Playful
Straight-forward
Spiritual
Rational Industrious
Dependable Accepting
Serene Modest
Reliable Peaceful

It's important to acknowledge our character assets as well as our defects. Make a list of your character assets. The above examples may be helpful. If you struggle, ask others what they think.

My Character Assets

Character Defects   Spiritual Principles

- ☐ Dishonest...Honest
- ☐ Selfish / Self-seeking...Interest in others
- ☐ Greed...Giving / Sharing
- ☐ Anger..Serenity / Calmness
- ☐ Lust..Purity / Healthy sexuality
- ☐ Envy...Gratitude
- ☐ Sloth...Action
- ☐ Gluttony...Moderation
- ☐ Pride...Humility
- ☐ Impatience...Patience
- ☐ Fear..Courage
- ☐ Intolerance..Tolerance
- ☐ Resentment...Forgiveness
- ☐ Hate..Love / Empathy
- ☐ Self-pity...Self-forgetfulness
- ☐ Self-importance..Modesty
- ☐ Inconsiderate...Considerate / Thoughtful
- ☐ Procrastination..Action
- ☐ Self-justification...Self-acceptance
- ☐ Self-condemnation..Self-forgiveness
- ☐ Suspicion...Trust
- ☐ Doubt..Faith
- ☐ Covetousness..Charity / Generosity
- ☐ Disrespect...Respect

Before we become entirely ready to have God remove our character defects, we must first know what they are. Thoroughly review your step 4 inventories, talk with your sponsor, and use the above list to help identify your personal defects of character, and note the corresponding spiritual principles.

Character Defects	Spiritual Principles
□ Critical	Non-judgemental
□ Impulsive	Considered actions
□ Stubborn	Open-minded
□ Ungrateful	Grateful
□ Pessimistic	Realistic
□ Self-centered	Caring
□ Manipulative	Non-controlling
□ Negative thinking	Positive thinking
□ Unfriendly	Friendly
□ Vain	Modest / Humble
□ Argumentative	Agreeable
□ Arrogant	Humble
□ False pride	Simplicity
□ Enabling	Setting boundaries
□ Perfectionist	Realistic goals
□ Self-destructive	Self-fulfilling
□ Unkind	Kind
□ Unsupportive	Supportive
□ Apathetic	Interested / Concerned
□ Gossiping	Kind / Praising
□ Untrustworthy	Trustworthy
□ Cynical	Open-minded
□ Indecisive	Decisive
□ Timid	Firm
□ Insecure	Self-confident
□ Irresponsible	Responsible
□ Superior	Humble

Step Six

My Character Defects

Write out your character defects from the previous page and add any others you've discovered

Spiritual Principles

Write out the corresponding spiritual principles

_____

_____

_____

_____

_____

_____

_____

_____

_____

_____

_____

_____

_____

_____

_____

_____

_____

_____

_____

1) How do I feel now that I've identified my character defects?

2) Can I see how some of my defects developed at a young age, and perhaps helped protect me in earlier life?

4) How does fear cause me to act on my defects of character?

3) Which unhealthy or unhelpful behaviours do I seem to repeat over and over?

*We were entirely ready to have God
remove all these defects of character*

5) Am I afraid that I won't be
able to change? To have
these defects removed?

6) How have I changed so far
since starting my recovery?

_____

_____

_____

_____

_____

_____

_____

_____

_____

_____

_____

_____

_____

_____

_____

_____

_____

_____

_____

_____

8) Do I have any fear about having my character defects removed?

7) What are my feelings about the prospect of having my defects of character removed?

> " *Much of our resistance to change is based in fear. We may find it easier to continue in an unhappy, yet familiar way of life, than to face an unknown and uncertain future. For many of us, our problems and shortcomings seemed to define us as people: what would we be without them? Often we find that our character defects started as ways to deal with difficult circumstances, in childhood or later. It is hard to let go of beliefs and behaviours that once helped us cope, or even kept us alive. If we are fearful, we can gently and courageously allow ourselves to consider the possibility of surrendering our familiar defects, trusting that our Higher Power will not give us more than we can handle.*

Sex Addicts Anonymous. (2014). *Sex Addicts Anonymous, 3rd Edition*. International Service Organization of SAA. p.40

> " When we are working Step Six, it is important to remember that we are human and should not place unrealistic expectations on ourselves. This is a step of willingness. That is the spiritual principle of Step Six. It is as if to say that we are now willing to move in a spiritual direction. Being human we will, of course, wander.

Adapted from: Alcoholics Anonymous. (1995). *Twelve Steps and Twelve Traditions*. New York: Alcoholics Anonymous World Services. p.65

We were entirely ready to have God remove all these defects of character

9) Which defects am I
most willing to let go of?

10) Which defects am I
reluctant to have removed?

....

....

....

....

....

....

....

....

....

....

....

....

....

....

....

....

....

....

....

....

....

....

12) How will the lives of those close to me be affected if I have my character defects removed?

11) How can my life be improved if I have these defects removed?

We were entirely ready to have God remove all these defects of character

13) Am I scared about what I will become once these defects are removed?

14) Is there anything holding me back from being entirely willing to have God remove my defects of character? Who can I discuss this with?

Step 6 Completion

I am now entirely ready to have God remove all of my defects of character.

Signed _____

Date _____

I am now ready for Step 7 ☐

Step Seven

We humbly asked Him to remove our shortcomings.

Now, in Step Seven, we humbly ask our Higher Power to remove our shortcomings. When we ask our Higher Power to remove these shortcomings, we ask for freedom from anything which limits our recovery. We ask for help because we cannot do it alone.

Narcotics Anonymous. (1993). *It Works, How and Why*. Chatsworth, California: Narcotics Anonymous World Services, Inc. p.69

Guidance

* Use these pages in whichever way serves you best

* Feel free to answer the suggested questions at the top of the pages

* Or instead, answer any questions your sponsor has recommended

* Use the blank pages at the back if you need more space

2) How has my relationship with my Higher Power developed since I started my recovery?

1) How has my understanding of my Higher Power developed since I started my recovery?

Step Seven

3) What am I most grateful for in my life?

4) What are my triggers for my addictive behaviours? What changes do I need to make to protect myself from these?

We humbly asked Him to remove our shortcomings

The Serenity Prayer

God, grant me the serenity to accept the things I cannot change, Courage to change the things I can, and wisdom to know the difference. Thy will, not mine, be done.

Step Seven

Alcoholics Anonymous. (1995). *Twelve Steps and Twelve Traditions*. New York: Alcoholics Anonymous World Services. p.41

7) Which of my character defects are the most dangerous to my life and my recovery?

8) What do I want to recapture in my life? Can the removal of my character defects help me do that?

We humbly asked Him to remove our shortcomings

" The Seventh Step is where we make the change in our attitude which permits us, with humility as our guide, to move out from ourselves toward others and toward God. The whole emphasis of Step Seven is on humility. It is really saying to us that we ought to be willing to try humility in seeking the removal of our shortcomings just as we did when we admitted that we were powerless over alcohol, and came to believe that a Power greater than ourselves could restore us to sanity. If that degree of humility could enable us to find the grace by which such a deadly obsession could be banished, then there must be hope of the same result respecting any other problem we could possibly have.

Adapted from: Alcoholics Anonymous. (1995). *Twelve Steps and Twelve Traditions*. New York: Alcoholics Anonymous World Services. p.76

66

This is our road to spiritual growth. We change every day. We gradually and carefully pull ourselves out of the isolation and loneliness of addiction and into the mainstream of life. This growth is not the result of wishing, but of action and prayer. The main objective of Step Seven is to get out of ourselves and strive to achieve the will of our Higher Power.

Narcotics Anonymous. (2008). *Narcotics Anonymous: 6th Edition Basic Text*. Chatsworth, California: NA World Services, Inc. p.37

10) How can I practice
being humble today?

9) What does humility
mean to me?

Step Seven

12) How does humility help me in my recovery and in working this step?

11) What are some examples of when I have practiced humility rather than arrogance, false pride or egotism? What were the results?

We humbly asked Him to remove our shortcomings

13) What situations, people or places cause me to regress back into my defects of character?

14) What can I do to lessen the chance of stresses and pressures causing me to revert to my character defects?

Step Seven

15) Which people and situations do I feel most supported by in my recovery?

16) Which people in recovery give me the most hope that character defects can be removed?

We humbly asked Him to remove our shortcomings

Step 7 Prayer from the 'The Big Book of AA':

My Creator, I am now willing that you should have all of me, good and bad. I pray that you now remove from me every single defect of character which stands in the way of my usefulness to you and my fellows. Grant me strength, as I go out from here, to do your bidding. Amen

Alcoholics Anonymous. (2001). *Alcoholics Anonymous, 4th Edition.* New York: A.A. World Services. p.76

Step 7 Prayer from *Drop the Rock:*

God (or Higher Power), thank You for the gift of my recovery and for all the benefits in my life. Please allow me to be open and grateful for the bounty of friends, family, growth, and much more in my life. Please help me gain an awareness of those shortcomings that hinder my service to others, myself, and You. Please help me find a way to remove those character defects in my life, both the ones I'm currently aware of and those that I may gain awareness of later. Help me become who and what I may become, in order to give more. Amen.

Bill P, Todd W, Sara S. (2005). *Drop The Rock, 2nd Edition.* Hazelden. P.81

Step 7 Completion

I have humbly asked Him to remove my shortcomings

Signed _____

Date _____

I am now ready for Step 8 ☐

Higher Power, I ask Your help in making my list of all those I have harmed. I will take responsibility for my mistakes, and be forgiving to others just as You are forgiving to me. Grant me the willingness to begin my restitution. This I pray.

Eighth Step Prayer. Bill P. and Lisa D. *The 12 Step Prayer Book. 2nd ed.* Center City, Minn.: Hazelden, 2004

Step Eight

We made a list of all
persons we had harmed,
and became willing to
make amends to them all

Guidance

* Use these pages in whichever way
  serves you best

* Feel free to answer the suggested
  questions on the right of the pages

* Or instead, answer any questions
  your sponsor has recommended

* Use the blank pages at the back if
  you need more space

Who I harmed *Person / institution*	What I did that was harmful	What I should have done instead

How my harm affected that person/institution	Am I willing to make amends *Yes / no*
....	
....	
....	
....	
....	
....	
....	
....	
....	
....	
....	
....	
....	
....	
....	
....	
....	
....	
....	
....	
....	

Reviewing your Step 4 inventories, complete this table

You can complete it row by row, or column by column

Use the blank pages at the back if you need more space

Continue on the next page

Who I harmed *Person / institution*	What I did that was harmful	What I should have done instead

How my harm affected that person/institution	Am I willing to make amends *Yes / no*

Reviewing your Step 4 inventories, complete this table

You can complete it row by row, or column by column

Use the blank pages at the back if you need more space

Continue on the next page

Who I harmed *Person / institution*	What I did that was harmful	What I should have done instead

How my harm affected that person/institution	Am I willing to make amends *Yes / no*

Reviewing your Step 4 inventories, complete this table

You can complete it row by row, or column by column

Use the blank pages at the back if you need more space

Continue on the next page

Who I harmed _Person / institution_	What I did that was harmful	What I should have done instead

How my harm affected that person/institution	Am I willing to make amends Yes / no

Reviewing your Step 4 inventories, complete this table

You can complete it row by row, or column by column

Use the blank pages at the back if you need more space

Continue on the next page

Who I harmed *Person / institution*	What I did that was harmful	What I should have done instead

How my harm affected that person/institution	Am I willing to make amends Yes / no

Reviewing your Step 4 inventories, complete this table

You can complete it row by row, or column by column

Use the blank pages at the back if you need more space

66

First, we take a look backward and try to discover where we have been at fault; next we make a vigorous attempt to repair the damage we have done; and third, having thus cleaned away the debris of the past, we consider how, with our newfound knowledge of ourselves, we may develop the best possible relations with every human being we know.

Alcoholics Anonymous. (1995). *Twelve Steps and Twelve Traditions*. New York: Alcoholics Anonymous World Services. p.77

" *While our efforts to make amends may make a difference in the lives of those we have harmed, this process has its greatest impact on our own lives. Our objective is to begin clearing away the damage we've done so that we can continue with our spiritual awakening. By the time we work our way through the process of making amends, we will surely be astounded by the level of freedom we feel.*

Narcotics Anonymous. (1993). *It Works, How and Why*. Chatsworth, California: Narcotics Anonymous World Services, Inc. p.77

Step Eight

1) Do I think my list is appropriate? Could I have too many or too few people on it? Who can I check with?

2) Being completely honest, is there anyone I've avoided putting on the list who should be on it?

3) What fears do I have about making amends to certain people?

4) Do I feel anger or resentment towards anyone on my list? How can re-visiting Step 4 help me with this?

We made a list of all persons we had harmed, and became willing to make amends to them all

Step Eight

5) Which people am I most willing to make amends to? Why?

6) Who am I not yet willing to make amends to? Why? Who can I discuss this with?

7) What have I done, or can I do to become willing to make these amends?

8) What's the worst thing that can happen when I make amends to someone?

We made a list of all persons we had harmed, and became willing to make amends to them all

Step Eight

9) What's the best thing that can happen when I make amends to someone?

10) What would my life be like if I had already made these amends?

Step 8 Completion

I have made a list of all persons I have harmed, and have become willing to make amends to them all

Signed _____

Date _____

I am now ready for Step 9 ☐

Higher Power, I pray for the right attitude to make my amends, being ever mindful not to harm others in the process. I ask for Your guidance in making indirect amends. Most important, I will continue to make amends by staying abstinent, helping others, and growing in spiritual progress.

Ninth Step Prayer. Bill P. and Lisa D. *The 12 Step Prayer Book. 2nd ed.* Center City, Minn.: Hazelden, 2004

Step Nine

We made direct amends to such people wherever possible, except when to do so would injure them or others

Guidance

* Use these pages in whichever way serves you best

* Feel free to answer the suggested questions at the bottom of the pages

* Or instead, answer any questions your sponsor has recommended

* Use the blank pages at the back if you need more space

Step 9 Promises from 'The Big Book of AA'

If we are painstaking about this phase of our development, we will be amazed before we are half way through. We are going to know a new freedom and a new happiness. We will not regret the past nor wish to shut the door on it. We will comprehend the word serenity and we will know peace. No matter how far down the scale we have gone, we will see how our experience can benefit others. That feeling of uselessness and self-pity will disappear. We will lose interest in selfish things and gain interest in our fellows. Self-seeking will slip away. Our whole attitude and outlook upon life will change. Fear of people and of economic insecurity will leave us. We will intuitively know how to handle situations which used to baffle us. We will suddenly realize that God is doing for us what we could not do for ourselves.

Are these extravagant promises? We think not. They are being fulfilled among us – sometimes quickly, sometimes slowly. They will always materialize if we work for them.

Alcoholics Anonymous. (2001). *Alcoholics Anonymous, 4th Edition*. New York: A.A. World Services. p.83-84.

Reflect on the Step 9 Promises

How do the promises make me feel?

What evidence do I have that the promises will be fulfilled for me?

How will these promises affect my life and the lives of others?

We made direct amends to such
people wherever possible, except when
to do so would injure them or others

....

....

....

....

....

....

....

....

....

....

....

....

....

....

....

....

....

....

....

....

....

....

Reviewing your Step 8 list, use these pages to put all of the people in
your list into the order that you are going to make amends to them

Many of us find it useful to start with the easiest ones and progress to the more difficult ones

Person or institution	Direct or indirect amends? Discuss with sponsor	How I will make amends Face-to-face, phone, letter etc

Use this table to plan your amends, in close discussion with your sponsor

Start by writing all the people from your list in the first column, in the order you wish to approach them

What will I say?	Completed	Outcome
Summarize the key points to include	Date	What were the results?

Starting with the first person on the list, complete the first 4 columns. Then once you've made the amends, complete the 5th and 6th columns

After each amends, move on to the next person on the list

Person *or institution*	Direct or indirect amends? *Discuss with sponsor*	How I will make amends *Face-to-face, phone, letter etc*

Use this table to plan your amends, in close discussion with your sponsor

Start by writing all the people from your list in the first column, in the order you wish to approach them

What will I say? Summarize the key points to include	Completed Date	Outcome What were the results?

Starting with the first person on the list, complete the first 4 columns. Then once you've made the amends, complete the 5th and 6th columns

After each amends, move on to the next person on the list

Person or institution	Direct or indirect amends? Discuss with sponsor	How I will make amends Face-to-face, phone, letter etc

Use this table to plan your amends, in close discussion with your sponsor

Start by writing all the people from your list in the first column, in the order you wish to approach them

What will I say?	Completed	Outcome
Summarize the key points to include	Date	What were the results?

Starting with the first person on the list, complete the first 4 columns. Then once you've made the amends, complete the 5th and 6th columns

After each amends, move on to the next person on the list

> *Now we go out to our fellows and repair the damage done in the past. We attempt to sweep away the debris which has accumulated out of our effort to live on self-will and run the show ourselves. If we haven't the will to do this, we ask until it comes.*

Alcoholics Anonymous. (2001). *Alcoholics Anonymous, 4th Edition*. New York: A.A. World Services. p.62. (AKA 'The Big Book of AA').

> In taking the Ninth Step, we act on the knowledge that what we do really matters - that our actions have consequences in the world, for good or ill. The damage we did in our addiction is cleared away not only by honestly admitting what we have done, but by committing to setting things right. Reaching out to others to acknowledge and heal the wrongs of the past brings us freedom and serenity in the present. We call this process making direct amends. In Step Nine we make our best effort to contact the people we have harmed, admit the wrongs we have done them, express our remorse, and offer some kind of reparation. Most importantly, we change how we behave today. We do our utmost not to repeat the behaviour that caused harm in the past, and we communicate this resolve to those we've hurt.

Sex Addicts Anonymous. (2014). *Sex Addicts Anonymous, 3rd Edition*. International Service Organization of SAA. p.48-49

Person or institution	Direct or indirect amends? Discuss with sponsor	How I will make amends Face-to-face, phone, letter etc

Use this table to plan your amends, in close discussion with your sponsor

Start by writing all the people from your list in the first column, in the order you wish to approach them

What will I say? Summarize the key points to include	Completed Date	Outcome What were the results?

Starting with the first person on the list, complete the first 4 columns. Then once you've made the amends, complete the 5th and 6th columns

After each amends, move on to the next person on the list

Person or institution	Direct or indirect amends? Discuss with sponsor	How I will make amends Face-to-face, phone, letter etc

Use this table to plan your amends, in close discussion with your sponsor

Start by writing all the people from your list in the first column, in the order you wish to approach them

What will I say?	Completed	Outcome
Summarize the key points to include	Date	What were the results?

Starting with the first person on the list, complete the first 4 columns. Then once you've made the amends, complete the 5th and 6th columns

After each amends, move on to the next person on the list

Person or institution	Direct or indirect amends? Discuss with sponsor	How I will make amends Face-to-face, phone, letter etc

Use this table to plan your amends, in close discussion with your sponsor

Start by writing all the people from your list in the first column, in the order you wish to approach them

What will I say? Summarize the key points to include	Completed Date	Outcome What were the results?

Starting with the first person on the list, complete the first 4 columns. Then once you've made the amends, complete the 5th and 6th columns

After each amends, move on to the next person on the list

We made direct amends to such people wherever possible, except when to do so would injure them or others

1) How do I feel now that I've completed my amends?

2) What have I learnt from this process?

Step 9 Completion

I have made direct amends to such people wherever possible, except when to do so would have injured them or others.

Signed   _____

Date   _____

I am now ready for Step 10 ☐

Step Ten

We continued to take personal inventory and when we were wrong promptly admitted it

I pray I may continue:
To grow in understanding and effectiveness;
To take daily spot-check inventories of myself;
To correct mistakes when I make them;
To take responsibility for my actions;
To be ever aware of my negative and self-defeating
attitudes and behaviors;
To keep my willfulness in check;
To always remember I need Your help;
To keep love and tolerance of others as my code;
And to continue in daily prayer how I can best
serve You, my Higher Power.

Tenth Step Prayer. Bill P. and Lisa D. The 12 Step Prayer Book. 2nd ed.
Center City, Minn.: Hazelden, 2004

Guidance

* Use these pages in whichever way serves you best

* There are a selection of spot-check and daily inventories
  to help build the habit of taking personal inventory

* Or instead, take inventory in a way agreed with your
  sponsor

* Use the blank pages at the back if you need more space

" A spot-check inventory taken in the midst of such disturbances can be of very great help in quieting stormy emotions. Today's spot check finds its chief application to situations which arise in each day's march. The consideration of long-standing difficulties had better be postponed, when possible, to times deliberately set aside for that purpose. The quick inventory is aimed at our daily ups and downs, especially those where people or new events throw us off balance and tempt us to make mistakes.

Alcoholics Anonymous. (1995). *Twelve Steps and Twelve Traditions*. New York: Alcoholics Anonymous World Services. p.90-91

Spot-check inventories

The pages ahead can be used "in the moment" at any time when you find yourself disturbed or off balance. There are some questions you can ask yourself, some common cognitive distortions to explore, and copies of the Step Four resentments, fears and harms inventories.

It is a spiritual axiom that every time we are disturbed, no matter what the cause, there is something wrong with us

Alcoholics Anonymous. (1995). *Twelve Steps and Twelve Traditions*. New York: Alcoholics Anonymous World Services. p.90

Questions to consider when tangled up

- Why am I angry, hurt, afraid?

- Is there something I'm failing to accept?

- Do I have an expectation that is not being fulfilled?

- Am I being loving and tolerant?

- Are any of the cognitive distortions on the next page playing a role here?

- Am I more interested in being right than being happy?

- Am I running on self-will?

- What is my role in this? How did I get the ball rolling?

- Am I accepting life on life's terms?

- What past hurts are being activated here?

Cognitive Distortions

Catastrophizing
Expecting disaster to strike
"I made a mistake at work, so I'll definitely get fired and everyone will hate me"

All or nothing thinking
Thinking in extremes, black and white, good or bad, nothing in between
"She's an angel, and I'm a complete failure"

Overgeneralizing
Making hasty generalizations with insufficient evidence, such as a single event
"I didn't do well at this, so I'll always fail"

Filtering
Dwelling on the negatives, and filtering out the positives

Mind reading
Assuming you know exactly what others are thinking (usually negative)

Fortune telling
Predicting how events will unfold, often to avoid trying something difficult

Musts and shoulds
Creating rules for how everyone should behave. Anger is generated when others break the rules, and guilt is the result when we break our own rules

Emotional reasoning
Assuming that your feelings must represent the truth
"I feel stupid, therefore it must be true"

Personalizing
Taking things personally when they are not connected to you or caused by you

Always being right
Going to any lengths to prove that you are right and others are wrong, often at the cost of other people's feelings

Labelling
Reducing people, including yourself, to a single—usually negative—label

Resentments

I'm resentful at:	The cause of my resentment	Which part(s) of self were affected?						
		Self esteem	Pride	Emotional security	Pocketbook	Ambitions	Personal relations	Sex relations

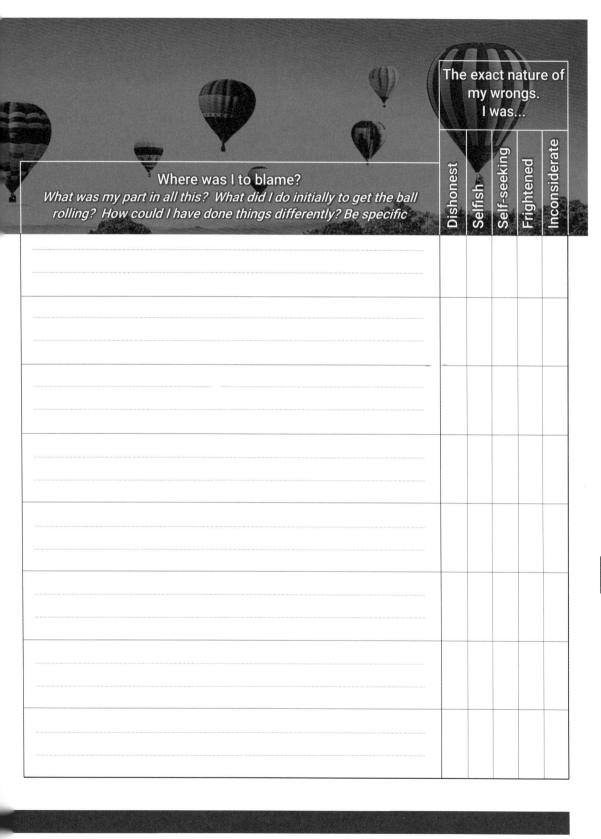

Where was I to blame? What was my part in all this? What did I do initially to get the ball rolling? How could I have done things differently? Be specific	The exact nature of my wrongs. I was...				
	Dishonest	Selfish	Self-seeking	Frightened	Inconsiderate

Resentments

I'm resentful at:	The cause of my resentment	Which part(s) of self were affected?						
		Self esteem	Pride	Emotional security	Pocketbook	Ambitions	Personal relations	Sex relations

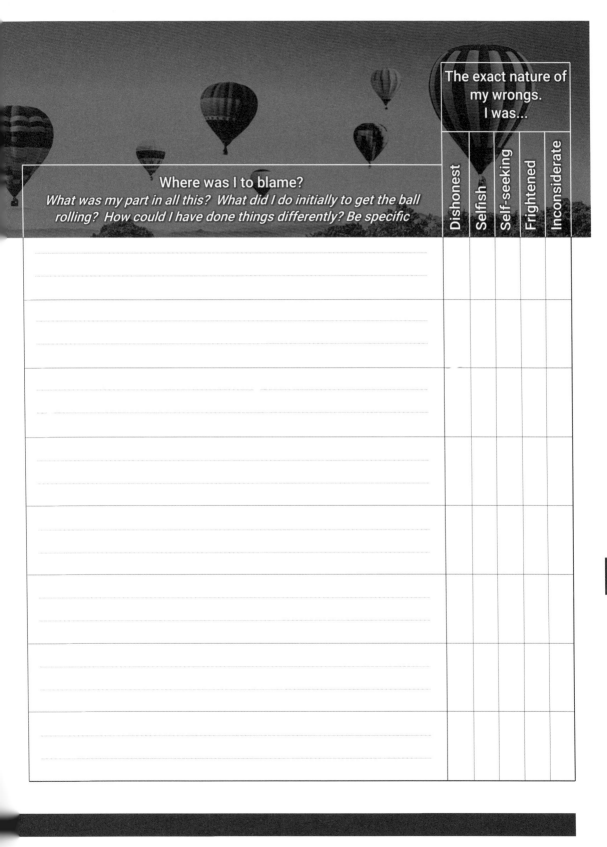

Where was I to blame? What was my part in all this? What did I do initially to get the ball rolling? How could I have done things differently? Be specific	The exact nature of my wrongs. I was...				
	Dishonest	Selfish	Self-seeking	Frightened	Inconsiderate

Resentments

I'm resentful at:	The cause of my resentment	Which part(s) of self were affected?						
		Self esteem	Pride	Emotional security	Pocketbook	Ambitions	Personal relations	Sex relations

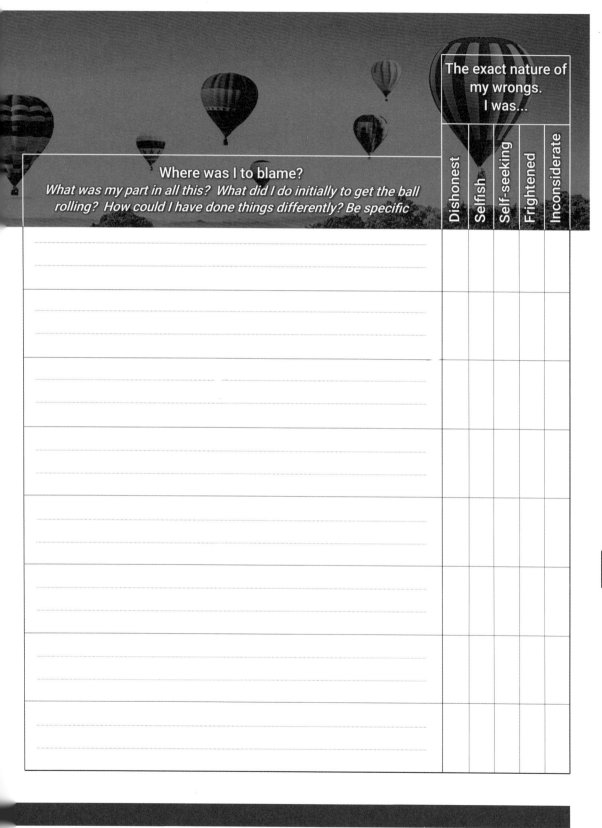

Where was I to blame? *What was my part in all this? What did I do initially to get the ball rolling? How could I have done things differently? Be specific*	The exact nature of my wrongs. I was...				
	Dishonest	Selfish	Self-seeking	Frightened	Inconsiderate

Fears

The fear	Why do I have this fear? What impacts or harms has this fear had on me and others?	Which part(s) of self have I been relying on which have failed me?			
		Self-reliance	Self-confidence	Self-discipline	Self-will

Which part(s) of self does the fear affect?							What was MY part in this? What did I do to get the ball rolling that led to my being in the position to have the fear?	Which character defects contributed to my actions or to me holding on to the old fear?				
Self esteem	Pride	Emotional security	Pocketbook	Ambitions	Personal relations	Sex relations		Dishonest	Selfish	Self-seeking	Frightened	Inconsiderate

Fears

The fear	Why do I have this fear? What impacts or harms has this fear had on me and others?	Which part(s) of self have I been relying on which have failed me?			
		Self-reliance	Self-confidence	Self-discipline	Self-will

Which part(s) of self does the fear affect?							What was MY part in this? What did I do to get the ball rolling that led to my being in the position to have the fear?	Which character defects contributed to my actions or to me holding on to the old fear?				
Self esteem	Pride	Emotional security	Pocketbook	Ambitions	Personal relations	Sex relations		Dishonest	Selfish	Self-seeking	Frightened	Inconsiderate

Fears

The fear	Why do I have this fear? What impacts or harms has this fear had on me and others?	Which part(s) of self have I been relying on which have failed me?			
		Self-reliance	Self-confidence	Self-discipline	Self-will

Which part(s) of self does the fear affect?							What was MY part in this? What did I do to get the ball rolling that led to my being in the position to have the fear?	Which character defects contributed to my actions or to me holding on to the old fear?				
Self esteem	Pride	Emotional security	Pocketbook	Ambitions	Personal relations	Sex relations		Dishonest	Selfish	Self-seeking	Frightened	Inconsiderate

Harms

Who did I harm? *People, institutions*	What did I do or fail to do to cause the harm?	Self esteem	Pride	Emotional security	Pocketbook	Ambitions	Personal relations	Sex relations

What feelings did I create in others? E.g. anger, fear, stress, sadness, shock, loneliness, jealousy	The exact nature of my wrongs. I was...					What should I have done instead? How would my Higher Power have me be instead? What can I do differently next time?
	Dishonest	Selfish	Self-seeking	Frightened	Inconsiderate	

Harms

Who did I harm? *People, institutions*	What did I do or fail to do to cause the harm?	Self esteem	Pride	Emotional security	Pocketbook	Ambitions	Personal relations	Sex relations

What feelings did I create in others? E.g. anger, fear, stress, sadness, shock, loneliness, jealousy	The exact nature of my wrongs. I was...					What should I have done instead? How would my Higher Power have me be instead? What can I do differently next time?
	Dishonest	Selfish	Self-seeking	Frightened	Inconsiderate	

Harms

Who did I harm? *People, institutions*	What did I do or fail to do to cause the harm?	Self esteem	Pride	Emotional security	Pocketbook	Ambitions	Personal relations	Sex relations

Which part(s) of self caused the harm?

What feelings did I create in others? *E.g. anger, fear, stress, sadness, shock, loneliness, jealousy*	The exact nature of my wrongs. I was...					What should I have done instead? *How would my Higher Power have me be instead?* *What can I do differently next time?*
	Dishonest	Selfish	Self-seeking	Frightened	Inconsiderate	

> 66

We have entered the world of the Spirit. Our next function is to grow in understanding and effectiveness. This is not an overnight matter. It should continue for our lifetime. Continue to watch for selfishness, dishonesty, resentment, and fear. When these crop up, we ask God at once to remove them. We discuss them with someone immediately and make amends quickly if we have harmed anyone. Then we resolutely turn our thoughts to someone we can help. Love and tolerance of others is our code.

Alcoholics Anonymous. (2001). *Alcoholics Anonymous, 4th Edition.* New York: A.A. World Services. p.84. (AKA 'The Big Book of AA').

Daily inventories

The pages ahead contain a variety of worksheets designed to help you continue to take personal inventory on a daily basis, and continue to set right any new mistakes as you go along

Date:

Have I been **selfish** today? How? Why?

Have I been **dishonest** today? How? Why?

Have I been resentful today?

At who? Why?

Affected my...

Self esteem ☐
Pride ☐
Emotional security ☐
Pocketbook ☐
Ambitions ☐
Personal relations ☐
Sex relations ☐

Where was I to blame?

I was...

Dishonest ☐
Selfish ☐
Self-seeking ☐
Frightened ☐
Inconsiderate ☐

Have I been fearful today?

Of what? Why?

What failed me?

Self-reliance ☐
Self-confidence ☐
Self-discipline ☐
Self-will ☐

What impact did the fear have on me?

What was my role in this?

"...when these crop up, we ask God at once to remove them..."

I have asked God to remove any selfishness, dishonesty, resentment or fear that cropped up today ☐

"...we discuss them with someone immediately..."

Who did I, or who will I, discuss them with?

"...and make amends quickly if we have harmed someone."

How I made, or will make, amends

Quotes: Alcoholics Anonymous. (2001). Alcoholics Anonymous, 4th Edition. New York: A.A. World Services. p.84.

Date:

Looking at my current behavior, am I living by my spiritual **values**?

Am I being **honest** today?

Am I maintaining personal **integrity** in my relations with others?

Am I **growing**, or am I slipping back into old patterns?

Quotes and questions adapted from: Narcotics Anonymous. (1993). It Works, How and Why. Chatsworth, California: Narcotics Anonymous World Services, Inc. p.99

Date: ....

How have I worked my program today?

....
....
....

What am I grateful for today?

....
....
....

What did I do today that I wish I had done differently?

....
....
....

What did I leave undone that I wish I had done?

....
....

Do I owe any amends today?

....
....
....

Did I allow myself to become obsessed by anything today?

....
....
....

Did I worry about the past or future today?

....
....
....

Was I happy and peaceful today?

....
....
....

Questions adapted from: Narcotics Anonymous. (1983). Living the Program. Narcotics anonymous World Services, Inc.

Date:

Did I connect with my Higher Power today?

Was there fear in my life today?

Have I harmed others, directly or indirectly, today? How?

Have I allowed myself to become too:

Hungry?

Angry?

Lonely?

Tired?

If I could do it again, what would I do differently?

Which of my character defects cropped up today?

Use one column per day. Each day, mark with a √ for being on the assets side
of the inventory, and a X for being on the liabilities side.

Liabilities to watch for	Date Feb 24									
Dishonesty	X									
Selfishness, self-seeking	√									
Fear	X									
Inconsiderate	√									
Resentful	√									
False pride	√									
Envy, jealousy	X									

Use the blank rows to add some of your own individual character defects from Step 6, along with their corresponding spiritual principles.

Date											**Assets** to strive for
											Honesty
											Interest in others
											Trust in Higher Power
											Considerate, thoughtful
											Forgiving
											Humility
											Contentment

Date:	*"Continue to watch for selfishness, dishonesty, resentment, and fear..."*

Have I been **selfish** today? How? Why?

Have I been **dishonest** today? How? Why?

Have I been **resentful** today?

At who? Why?

Affected my...

Self esteem	☐
Pride	☐
Emotional security	☐
Pocketbook	☐
Ambitions	☐
Personal relations	☐
Sex relations	☐

Where was I to blame?

I was...

Dishonest	☐
Selfish	☐
Self-seeking	☐
Frightened	☐
Inconsiderate	☐

Have I been **fearful** today?

Of what? Why?

What failed me?

Self-reliance	☐
Self-confidence	☐
Self-discipline	☐
Self-will	☐

What impact did the fear have on me?

What was my role in this?

"...when these crop up, we ask God at once to remove them..."

I have asked God to remove any selfishness, dishonesty, resentment or fear that cropped up today ☐

"...we discuss them with someone immediately..."

Who did I, or who will I, discuss them with?

"...and make amends quickly if we have harmed someone."

How I made, or will make, amends

Quotes: Alcoholics Anonymous. (2001). Alcoholics Anonymous, 4th Edition. New York: A.A. World Services. p.84.

Date:

"We ask ourselves the same types of questions we asked in the Fourth Step; the only difference is that the emphasis is on today."

Looking at my current behavior, am I living by my spiritual **values**?

Am I being **honest** today?

Am I maintaining personal **integrity** in my relations with others?

Am I **growing**, or am I slipping back into old patterns?

"In order to examine our day – or our life, for that matter – in its entirety, we have to draw on the humility we've acquired in the previous steps."

Date: ....

How have I worked my program today?

....
....
....
....

What am I grateful for today?

....
....
....
....

What did I do today that I wish I had done differently?

....
....
....
....

What did I leave undone that I wish I had done?

....
....
....

Do I owe any amends today?

....
....
....
....

Did I allow myself to become obsessed by anything today?

....
....
....

Did I worry about the past or future today?

....
....
....
....

Was I happy and peaceful today?

....
....
....
....

Questions adapted from: Narcotics Anonymous. (1983). Living the Program. Narcotics anonymous World Services, Inc.

Date:

Did I connect with my Higher Power today?

Was there fear in my life today?

Have I harmed others, directly or indirectly, today? How?

Have I allowed myself to become too:

Hungry?

Angry?

Lonely?

Tired?

If I could do it again, what would I do differently?

Which of my character defects cropped up today?

Date:	*"Continue to watch for selfishness, dishonesty, resentment, and fear..."*

Have I been selfish today? How? Why?

Have I been dishonest today? How? Why?

Have I been resentful today?

At who? Why?

Affected my...

- Self esteem ☐
- Pride ☐
- Emotional security ☐
- Pocketbook ☐
- Ambitions ☐
- Personal relations ☐
- Sex relations ☐

Where was I to blame?

I was...

- Dishonest ☐
- Selfish ☐
- Self-seeking ☐
- Frightened ☐
- Inconsiderate ☐

Have I been fearful today?

Of what? Why?

What failed me?

- Self-reliance ☐
- Self-confidence ☐
- Self-discipline ☐
- Self-will ☐

What impact did the fear have on me?

What was my role in this?

"...when these crop up, we ask God at once to remove them..."

I have asked God to remove any selfishness, dishonesty, resentment or fear that cropped up today   ☐

"...we discuss them with someone immediately..."

Who did I, or who will I, discuss them with?

"...and make amends quickly if we have harmed someone."

How I made, or will make, amends

Quotes: Alcoholics Anonymous. (2001). Alcoholics Anonymous, 4th Edition. New York: A.A. World Services. p.84.

Date:

Looking at my current behavior, am I living by my spiritual **values**?

Am I being **honest** today?

Am I maintaining personal **integrity** in my relations with others?

Am I **growing**, or am I slipping back into old patterns?

Quotes and questions adapted from: Narcotics Anonymous. (1993). It Works, How and Why. Chatsworth, California: Narcotics Anonymous World Services, Inc. p.99

Date: _____

How have I worked my **program** today?

_____
_____
_____
_____

What am I **grateful** for today?

_____
_____
_____
_____

What did I do today that I wish I had done differently?

_____
_____
_____

What did I leave undone that I wish I had done?

_____
_____
_____

Do I owe any **amends** today?

_____
_____
_____
_____

Did I allow myself to become **obsessed** by anything today?

_____
_____
_____

Did I **worry** about the past or future today?

_____
_____
_____

Was I **happy** and **peaceful** today?

_____
_____
_____

Questions adapted from: Narcotics Anonymous. (1983). Living the Program. Narcotics anonymous World Services, Inc.

Date:

Did I connect with my Higher Power today?

Was there fear in my life today?

Have I harmed others, directly or indirectly, today? How?

Have I allowed myself to become too:

Hungry?
Angry?
Lonely?
Tired?

If I could do it again, what would I do differently?

Which of my character defects cropped up today?

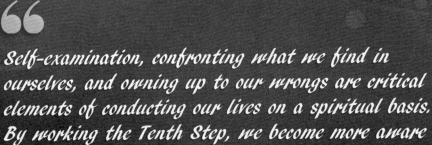

"

Self-examination, confronting what we find in ourselves, and owning up to our wrongs are critical elements of conducting our lives on a spiritual basis. By working the Tenth Step, we become more aware of our emotions, our mental state, and our spiritual condition. As we do, we find ourselves constantly rewarded with fresh insight.

Narcotics Anonymous. (1993). It Works, How and Why. Chatsworth, California: Narcotics Anonymous World Services, Inc. p.96

> *Regular inventory is the cornerstone of the Tenth Step. We set aside time to review our behaviour, our dealings with others, our emotions, and our spiritual condition. Quiet time for self-reflection, without distraction, is essential. We may each find different ways to set aside this time, and different methods for taking stock. However we work this step, we act on our commitment to making continued self-examination part of our new way of life.*

Sex Addicts Anonymous. (2014). Sex Addicts Anonymous, 3rd Edition. International Service Organization of SAA. p.52

Use one column per day. Each day, mark with a √ for being on the assets side of the inventory, and a X for being on the liabilities side.

Liabilities to watch for	Date										
Dishonesty											
Selfishness, self-seeking											
Fear											
Inconsiderate											
Resentful											
False pride											
Envy, jealousy											

Use the blank rows to add some of your own individual character defects from Step 6, along with their corresponding spiritual principles.

Date										**Assets** to strive for
										Honesty
										Love, interest in others
										Trust in Higher Power
										Considerate, thoughtful
										Forgiving
										Humility
										Contentment

Date:

Have I been **selfish** today? How? Why?

Have I been **dishonest** today? How? Why?

Have I been <u>**resentful** today?</u>

At who? Why?

Where was I to blame?

Affected my...

Self esteem	☐
Pride	☐
Emotional security	☐
Pocketbook	☐
Ambitions	☐
Personal relations	☐
Sex relations	☐

I was...

Dishonest	☐
Selfish	☐
Self-seeking	☐
Frightened	☐
Inconsiderate	☐

Have I been <u>**fearful** today?</u>

Of what? Why?

What failed me?

Self-reliance	☐
Self-confidence	☐
Self-discipline	☐
Self-will	☐

What impact did the fear have on me?

What was my role in this?

"...when these crop up, we ask God at once to remove them..."

I have asked God to remove any selfishness, dishonesty, resentment or fear that cropped up today ☐

"...we discuss them with someone immediately..."

Who did I, or who will I, discuss them with?

"...and make amends quickly if we have harmed someone."

How I made, or will make, amends

Quotes: Alcoholics Anonymous. (2001). Alcoholics Anonymous, 4th Edition. New York: A.A. World Services. p.84.

Date:

Looking at my current behavior, am I living by my spiritual **values**?

Am I being **honest** today?

Am I maintaining personal **integrity** in my relations with others?

Am I **growing**, or am I slipping back into old patterns?

Quotes and questions adapted from: Narcotics Anonymous. (1993). It Works, How and Why. Chatsworth, California: Narcotics Anonymous World Services, Inc. p.99

Date:

How have I worked my **program** today?

What am I **grateful** for today?

What did I do today that I wish I had done differently?

What did I leave undone that I wish I had done?

Do I owe any **amends** today?

Did I allow myself to become **obsessed** by anything today?

Did I **worry** about the past or future today?

Was I **happy** and **peaceful** today?

Date:

Did I connect with my **Higher Power** today?

Was there **fear** in my life today?

Have I **harmed** others, directly or indirectly, today? How?

Have I allowed myself to become too:

Hungry?

Angry?

Lonely?

Tired?

If I could do it again, what would I do differently?

Which of my **character defects** cropped up today?

Date:

"Continue to watch for selfishness, dishonesty, resentment, and fear..."

Have I been **selfish** today? How? Why?

Have I been **dishonest** today? How? Why?

Have I been **resentful** today?

At who? Why?

Affected my...

- Self esteem ☐
- Pride ☐
- Emotional security ☐
- Pocketbook ☐
- Ambitions ☐
- Personal relations ☐
- Sex relations ☐

Where was I to blame?

I was...

- Dishonest ☐
- Selfish ☐
- Self-seeking ☐
- Frightened ☐
- Inconsiderate ☐

Have I been **fearful** today?

Of what? Why?

What failed me?

- Self-reliance ☐
- Self-confidence ☐
- Self-discipline ☐
- Self-will ☐

What impact did the fear have on me?

What was my role in this?

"...when these crop up, we ask God at once to remove them..."

I have asked God to remove any selfishness, dishonesty, resentment or fear that cropped up today ☐

"...we discuss them with someone immediately..."

Who did I, or who will I, discuss them with?

"...and make amends quickly if we have harmed someone."

How I made, or will make, amends

Quotes: Alcoholics Anonymous. (2001). Alcoholics Anonymous, 4th Edition. New York: A.A. World Services. p.84.

Date:

_____

Looking at my current behavior, am I living by my spiritual **values**?

Am I being **honest** today?

Am I maintaining personal **integrity** in my relations with others?

Am I **growing**, or am I slipping back into old patterns?

Date: ....

How have I worked my program today?

....
....
....
....

What am I grateful for today?

....
....
....
....

What did I do today that I wish I had done differently?

....
....
....

What did I leave undone that I wish I had done?

....
....
....

Do I owe any amends today?

....
....
....

Did I allow myself to become obsessed by anything today?

....
....
....

Did I worry about the past or future today?

....
....
....

Was I happy and peaceful today?

....
....
....

Questions adapted from: Narcotics Anonymous. (1983). Living the Program. Narcotics anonymous World Services, Inc.

Date:

Did I connect with my **Higher Power** today?

Was there **fear** in my life today?

Have I **harmed** others, directly or indirectly, today? How?

Have I allowed myself to become too:

Hungry?

Angry?

Lonely?

Tired?

If I could do it again, what would I do differently?

Which of my **character defects** cropped up today?

Date: _____

"Continue to watch for selfishness, dishonesty, resentment, and fear..."

Have I been **selfish** today? How? Why?

Have I been **dishonest** today? How? Why?

Have I been <u>resentful</u> today?
At who? Why?

Affected my...

Self esteem	☐
Pride	☐
Emotional security	☐
Pocketbook	☐
Ambitions	☐
Personal relations	☐
Sex relations	☐

Where was I to blame?

I was...

Dishonest	☐
Selfish	☐
Self-seeking	☐
Frightened	☐
Inconsiderate	☐

Have I been <u>fearful</u> today?
Of what? Why?

What failed me?

Self-reliance	☐
Self-confidence	☐
Self-discipline	☐
Self-will	☐

What impact did the fear have on me?

What was my role in this?

"...when these crop up, we ask God at once to remove them..."

I have asked God to remove any selfishness, dishonesty, resentment or fear that cropped up today ☐

"...we discuss them with someone immediately..."

Who did I, or who will I, discuss them with? _____

"...and make amends quickly if we have harmed someone."

How I made, or will make, amends _____

Quotes: Alcoholics Anonymous. (2001). Alcoholics Anonymous, 4th Edition. New York: A.A. World Services. p.84.

Date:

Looking at my current behavior, am I living by my spiritual **values**?

Am I being **honest** today?

Am I maintaining personal **integrity** in my relations with others?

Am I **growing**, or am I slipping back into old patterns?

Quotes and questions adapted from: Narcotics Anonymous. (1993). It Works, How and Why. Chatsworth, California: Narcotics Anonymous World Services, Inc. p.99

Date: ....

How have I worked my program today?

....
....
....
....

What am I grateful for today?

....
....
....
....

What did I do today that I wish I had done differently?

....
....
....
....

What did I leave undone that I wish I had done?

....
....
....

Do I owe any amends today?

....
....
....
....

Did I allow myself to become obsessed by anything today?

....
....
....

Did I worry about the past or future today?

....
....
....
....

Was I happy and peaceful today?

....
....
....
....

Questions adapted from: Narcotics Anonymous. (1983). Living the Program. Narcotics anonymous World Services, Inc.

Date: _____

Did I connect with my Higher Power today?

_____
_____
_____
_____

Was there fear in my life today?

_____
_____
_____
_____

Have I harmed others, directly or indirectly, today? How?

_____
_____
_____
_____

Have I allowed myself to become too:

Hungry? _____
Angry? _____
Lonely? _____
Tired? _____

If I could do it again, what would I do differently?

_____
_____
_____
_____

Which of my character defects cropped up today?

_____
_____
_____
_____

Date:

Have I been selfish today? How? Why?

Have I been dishonest today? How? Why?

Have I been resentful today?

At who? Why?

Affected my...
- Self esteem ☐
- Pride ☐
- Emotional security ☐
- Pocketbook ☐
- Ambitions ☐
- Personal relations ☐
- Sex relations ☐

Where was I to blame?

I was...
- Dishonest ☐
- Selfish ☐
- Self-seeking ☐
- Frightened ☐
- Inconsiderate ☐

Have I been fearful today?

Of what? Why?

What failed me?
- Self-reliance ☐
- Self-confidence ☐
- Self-discipline ☐
- Self-will ☐

What impact did the fear have on me?

What was my role in this?

"...When these crop up, we ask God at once to remove them..."

I have asked God to remove any selfishness, dishonesty, resentment or fear that cropped up today ☐

"...We discuss them with someone immediately..."

Who did I, or who will I, discuss them with?

"...And make amends quickly if we have harmed someone."

How I made, or will make, amends

Quotes: Alcoholics Anonymous. (2001). Alcoholics Anonymous, 4th Edition. New York: A.A. World Services. p.84.

Step 10 Completion

I am continuing to take
personal inventory and when
I am wrong, I promptly
admit it.

Signed _____

Date _____

I am now ready for Step 11 ☐

Step Eleven

We sought through prayer and meditation to improve our conscious contact with God *as we understood Him,* praying only for knowledge of His will for us and the power to carry that out.

Higher Power, as I understand You, I pray to keep open my connection with You and to keep it clear from the confusion of daily life. Through my prayers and meditations I ask especially for freedom from self-will, rationalization, and wishful thinking. I pray for the guidance of correct thought and positive action. Your will, Higher Power, not mine, be done.

Eleventh Step Prayer. Bill P. and Lisa D. *The 12 Step Prayer Book. 2nd ed.* Center City, Minn.: Hazelden, 2004

Guidance

* Use these pages in whichever way serves you best

* Feel free to answer the suggested questions at the bottom of the pages

* Or instead, answer any questions your sponsor has recommended

* Use the blank pages at the back if you need more space

Some prayers from the 'Big Book' of AA

On awakening, pray:

(p.86)

God, I ask you to direct my thinking, I especially ask that my thinking be divorced from self-pity, dishonest or self-seeking motives.

Think about the twenty-four hours ahead, consider your plans for the day. Then pray:

(p.87)

God, I pray that I be shown all through the day what my next step is to be. I pray that I be given whatever I need to take care of such problems. I ask especially for freedom from self-will. I ask that I be given strength only if others will be helped.

If faced with indecision, pray:
Then relax, take it easy, don't struggle
(p.86)

I ask you for inspiration, an intuitive thought, or a decision.

Other useful prayers:
(p.83)

My creator, I ask that you show me the way of patience, tolerance, kindliness and love.

(p.164)

God, what can I do today for the man who is still sick?

| Constantly remind yourself: (p.87-88) | *I am no longer running the show* |

| Say to yourself throughout the day: (p.88) | *Thy will be done* |

| When agitated or doubtful: (p.87) | *God, please give me the right thought or action* |

| Thoughts which must go with you constantly: (p.85) | *How can I best serve thee?*
 Thy will (not mine) be done. |

| If a person offends you: (p.67) | *This is a sick man. How can I be helpful to him?*
 God save me from being angry. Thy will be done. |

| In the evening, after constructively reviewing the day: (p.86) | *God, please forgive me and tell me what corrective measures should be taken.* |

Alcoholics Anonymous. (2001). Alcoholics Anonymous, 4th Edition. New York: A.A. World Services.

We sought through prayer and meditation to improve our conscious contact with God as we understood Him, praying only for knowledge of His will for us and the power to carry that out

....

....

....

....

....

....

....

....

....

....

....

....

....

....

....

....

....

....

....

1) How has my understanding of my Higher Power developed since starting recovery?

2) Based on my current understanding, what qualities does my Higher Power have?

3) What have I done or am I
doing to explore my spirituality?

4) What feelings do I have about prayer?

We sought through prayer and meditation to improve our conscious contact with God as we understood Him, praying only for knowledge of His will for us and the power to carry that out

6) How has prayer helped me put things into perspective?

5) How do I pray?

8) What can I do to make my prayer
life more consistent and effective?

7) What effects has praying
had in my life so far?

10) Which aspects of the prayer can I strive to apply to my life?

9) What feelings do I have about the Prayer of St Francis of Assisi?

Prayer of Saint Francis of Assisi

Lord, make me a channel of thy peace;

That where there is hatred, I may bring love;

That where there is wrong, I may bring the spirit of forgiveness;

That where there is discord, I may bring harmony;

That where there is error, I may bring truth;

That where there is doubt, I may bring faith;

That where there is despair, I may bring hope;

That where there are shadows, I may bring light;

That where there is sadness, I may bring joy.

Lord, grant that I may seek rather to comfort than to be comforted;

To understand, than to be understood;

To love, than to be loved.

For it is by self-forgetting that one finds.

It is by forgiving that one is forgiven.

It is by dying that one awakens to Eternal Life.

Amen

Alcoholics Anonymous. (1995). *Twelve Steps and Twelve Traditions*. New York: Alcoholics Anonymous World Services. p.99

> 66 *Prayer and meditation are our principal means of conscious contact with God.*
>
> *...Of course we finally did experiment, and when unexpected results followed, we felt different; in fact we knew different; and so we were sold on meditation and prayer. And that, we have found, can happen to anybody who tries. It has been well said that "almost the only scoffers at prayer are those who never tried it enough".*

Alcoholics Anonymous. (1995). *Twelve Steps and Twelve Traditions*. New York: Alcoholics Anonymous World Services. p.96-97

In taking the Eleventh Step, we dedicate ourselves to an increasing spiritual awareness and a greater connection with our Higher Power. As we progress in recovery, we come to realize that our Higher Power has always been with us, even in the depths of our addiction. It is our conscious contact with this Power that has increased for us as we work through each step. By making contact with God a conscious practice, we have allowed God into our lives, healing us, directing us, and changing us in ways that were never possible before. In Step Eleven we seek to improve this conscious contact, so that our spiritual connection will become not only the means by which we recover from our addiction, but our daily source of guidance and strength.

Adapted from: Sex Addicts Anonymous. (2014). *Sex Addicts Anonymous, 3rd Edition*. International Service Organization of SAA. p.55

We sought through prayer and meditation to improve our conscious contact with God as we understood Him, praying only for knowledge of His will for us and the power to carry that out

11) What's my understanding of meditation?

12) How do I feel about meditation as a concept?

13) Who do I know that regularly meditates? What's their experience been?

14) How can meditation help me build a relationship with my Higher Power?

We sought through prayer and meditation to improve our conscious contact with God as we understood Him, praying only for knowledge of His will for us and the power to carry that out

....

....

....

....

....

....

....

....

....

....

....

....

....

....

....

....

....

....

16) Am I aware of the presence of my Higher Power in my life? In what ways? What does it feel like?

15) If I've been meditating for some time, what effects has it had on my life?

17) What am I doing to improve my conscious contact with God as I understand Him?

18) What do I think God's will for me is? How can I try to better understand it?

> ❝ *When we retire at night, we constructively review our day...*
>
> *...But we must be careful not to drift into worry, remorse or morbid reflection, for that would diminish our usefulness to others. After making our review we ask God's forgiveness and inquire what corrective measures should be taken.*

Alcoholics Anonymous. (2001). Alcoholics Anonymous, 4th Edition. New York: A.A. World Services. p.86. (AKA 'The Big Book of AA').

Constructive Daily Reviews

The pages ahead are designed to help us get into the habit of reviewing our day. Questions have been taken from *The Big Book of AA.*

Was I resentful, selfish, dishonest or afraid?

Do I owe an apology?

Have I kept something to myself which should be discussed with another person at once?

Was I kind and loving towards all?

What could I have done better?

Was I thinking of myself most of the time? Or was I thinking of what I could do for others, of what I could pack into the stream of life?

Was I resentful, selfish, dishonest or afraid?

Do I owe an apology?

Have I kept something to myself which should be discussed with another person at once?

Was I kind and loving towards all?

What could I have done better?

Was I thinking of myself most of the time? Or was I thinking of what I could do for others, of what I could pack into the stream of life?

Was I resentful, selfish, dishonest or afraid?

Do I owe an apology?

Have I kept something to myself which should be discussed with another person at once?

Was I kind and loving towards all?

What could I have done better?

Was I thinking of myself most of the time? Or was I thinking of what I could do for others, of what I could pack into the stream of life?

Was I resentful, selfish, dishonest or afraid?

Do I owe an apology?

Have I kept something to myself which should be discussed with another person at once?

Was I kind and loving towards all?

What could I have done better?

Was I thinking of myself most of the time? Or was I thinking of what I could do for others, of what I could pack into the stream of life?

Was I resentful, selfish, dishonest or afraid?

Do I owe an apology?

Have I kept something to myself which should be discussed with another person at once?

Was I kind and loving towards all?

What could I have done better?

Was I thinking of myself most of the time? Or was I thinking of what I could do for others, of what I could pack into the stream of life?

Was I resentful, selfish, dishonest or afraid?

Do I owe an apology?

Have I kept something to myself which should be discussed with another person at once?

Was I kind and loving towards all?

What could I have done better?

Was I thinking of myself most of the time? Or was I thinking of what I could do for others, of what I could pack into the stream of life?

Was I resentful, selfish, dishonest or afraid?

Do I owe an apology?

Have I kept something to myself which should be discussed with another person at once?

Was I kind and loving towards all?

What could I have done better?

Was I thinking of myself most of the time? Or was I thinking of what I could do for others, of what I could pack into the stream of life?

Was I resentful, selfish, dishonest or afraid?

Do I owe an apology?

Have I kept something to myself which should be discussed with another person at once?

Was I kind and loving towards all?

What could I have done better?

Was I thinking of myself most of the time? Or was I thinking of what I could do for others, of what I could pack into the stream of life?

Alcoholics Anonymous. (2001). Alcoholics Anonymous, 4th Edition. New York: A.A. World Services. p.86

Was I resentful, selfish, dishonest or afraid?

Do I owe an apology?

Have I kept something to myself which should be discussed with another person at once?

Was I kind and loving towards all?

What could I have done better?

Was I thinking of myself most of the time? Or was I thinking of what I could do for others, of what I could pack into the stream of life?

Was I resentful, selfish, dishonest or afraid?

Do I owe an apology?

Have I kept something to myself which should be discussed with another person at once?

Was I kind and loving towards all?

What could I have done better?

Was I thinking of myself most of the time? Or was I thinking of what I could do for others, of what I could pack into the stream of life?

Was I resentful, selfish, dishonest or afraid?

Do I owe an apology?

Have I kept something to myself which should be discussed with another person at once?

Was I kind and loving towards all?

What could I have done better?

Was I thinking of myself most of the time? Or was I thinking of what I could do for others, of what I could pack into the stream of life?

Was I resentful, selfish, dishonest or afraid?

Do I owe an apology?

Have I kept something to myself which should be discussed with another person at once?

Was I kind and loving towards all?

What could I have done better?

Was I thinking of myself most of the time? Or was I thinking of what I could do for others, of what I could pack into the stream of life?

Was I resentful, selfish, dishonest or afraid?

Do I owe an apology?

Have I kept something to myself which should be discussed with another person at once?

Was I kind and loving towards all?

What could I have done better?

Was I thinking of myself most of the time? Or was I thinking of what I could do for others, of what I could pack into the stream of life?

Was I resentful, selfish, dishonest or afraid?

Do I owe an apology?

Have I kept something to myself which should be discussed with another person at once?

Was I kind and loving towards all?

What could I have done better?

Was I thinking of myself most of the time? Or was I thinking of what I could do for others, of what I could pack into the stream of life?

Was I resentful, selfish, dishonest or afraid?

Do I owe an apology?

Have I kept something to myself which should be discussed with another person at once?

Was I kind and loving towards all?

What could I have done better?

Was I thinking of myself most of the time? Or was I thinking of what I could do for others, of what I could pack into the stream of life?

Was I resentful, selfish, dishonest or afraid?

Do I owe an apology?

Have I kept something to myself which should be discussed with another person at once?

Was I kind and loving towards all?

What could I have done better?

Was I thinking of myself most of the time? Or was I thinking of what I could do for others, of what I could pack into the stream of life?

Alcoholics Anonymous. (2001). Alcoholics Anonymous, 4th Edition. New York: A.A. World Services. p.86

19) Am I managing to pray and meditate each day? If not, what's stopping me?

Step 11 Completion

I continue to seek, through prayer and meditation, to improve my conscious contact with God as I understand Him, praying only for knowledge of His will for me and the power to carry that out.

Signed   _____

Date   _____

I am now ready for Step 12 ☐

Step Twelve

Having had a spiritual awakening as the result of these steps, we tried to carry this message to other addicts, and to practice these principles in all our affairs

- Use these pages in whichever way serves you best

- Feel free to answer the suggested questions at the top of the pages

- Or instead, answer any questions your sponsor has recommended

- Use the blank pages at the back if you need more space

Dear God,
My spiritual awakening continues to unfold. The help I have received I shall pass on and give to others, both in and out of the Fellowship. For this opportunity I am grateful.
I pray most humbly to continue walking day by day on the road of spiritual progress. I pray for the inner strength and wisdom to practice the principles of this way of life in all I do and say. I need You, my friends, and the Program every hour of every day. This is a better way to live.

Twelfth Step Prayer. Bill P. and Lisa D. *The 12 Step Prayer Book. 2nd ed.*
Center City, Minn.: Hazelden, 2004

As we turn our attention to carrying the message, it's helpful to take stock of all we have achieved as a result of working the steps. While, everyone's spiritual awakening is different, below are some commonly reported themes. Take some time to look back and reflect on all the progress made so far. Getting clear about your own spiritual awakening will make you more effective at carrying the message of recovery to other addicts.

Step Twelve

Sense of purpose

Feeling more light-hearted

Humility

Caring more about others

Freedom from fear

Ability to step outside ourselves and participate fully in life

Inner peace   Growing intuition

Openness   Improved or transformed relationships

Expansion   Serenity

Feeling free

Acceptance   Freedom from guilt and shame

Growing self-acceptance

Laughter

Desire for authenticity

Joy   Self-expression

Living in the present

Happiness   Unconditional love

Sense of gratitude   Harmony with others

No regrets   Clarity of mind

Growing compassion

Trust and faith

Ability to forgive others and ourselves

Desire for honesty and integrity

Ease   Desire to help others

My Spiritual Awakening

1) What are some of the ways that the message of recovery has been carried to me? How effective were they?

2) How am I carrying the message to other addicts?

Step Twelve

3) What else could I be doing to carry the message?

4) How has my ego prevented me from effectively carrying the message?

Having had a spiritual awakening as a result of these steps, we tried to carry this message to other addicts, and to practice these principles in all our affairs

5) How does carrying the message help me?

6) What specific commitments can I make to carry the message to other addicts?

Step Twelve

66

Step Twelve has a paradoxical aspect in that the more we help others, the more we help ourselves. For instance, if we find ourselves troubled and our faith wavering, there are very few actions that have such an immediate uplifting effect on us as helping a newcomer. One small act of generosity can work wonders; our self-absorption diminishes and we end up with a better perspective on what previously seemed like overwhelming problems.

Narcotics Anonymous. (1993). *It Works, How and Why*. Chatsworth, California: Narcotics Anonymous World Services, Inc. p.118

7) What qualities does my sponsor have that have helped our relationship and my recovery?

8) Why was I able to accept help and guidance from those in recovery, but not from others?

Step Twelve

9) Reviewing Steps 6 and 7, which spiritual principles do I personally need to practice the most?

10) Which other spiritual principles have I learned about while working the steps, that I need to also practice?

Having had a spiritual awakening as a result of these steps, we tried to carry this message to other addicts, and to practice these principles in all our affairs

11) What are some ways I can practice these principles...

...With my family?

...With my friends, acquaintances, others in recovery?

...At work?   ...In other areas of my life?

_____
_____
_____
_____
_____
_____
_____
_____
_____
_____
_____
_____
_____
_____
_____
_____
_____

Having had a spiritual awakening as a result of these steps, we tried to carry this message to other addicts, and to practice these principles in all our affairs

"

The Steps are an expression of spiritual principles that can be practiced in all aspects of life. Honesty, willingness, courage, humility, forgiveness, responsibility, gratitude, and faith are just some of the names we give to the spiritual principles that gradually come to guide us in our lives. As we progress through the program, establishing conscious contact with the God of our understanding, we become aware of these principles within us – like gifts that were always there, unopened until we were ready to receive them. Opening these gifts brings about our spiritual awakening. Continuing to apply them on a daily basis keeps us spiritually fit and growing in recovery.

Adapted from: Sex Addicts Anonymous. (2014). *Sex Addicts Anonymous, 3rd Edition*. International Service Organization of SAA. p.60-61

66 *Here we experience the kind of giving that asks no rewards. Here we begin to practice all Twelve Steps of the program in our daily lives so that we and those about us may find emotional sobriety. When the Twelfth Step is seen in its full implication, it is really talking about the kind of love that has no price tag on it.*

Alcoholics Anonymous. (1995). *Twelve Steps and Twelve Traditions*. New York: Alcoholics Anonymous World Services. p.106

12) Which of these principles do I find most difficult to practice? Why?

13) In what situations do I find it difficult to practice these spiritual principles? Why? Who can I talk to about this?

Step Twelve

Step 12 Completion

*Having had a spiritual
awakening as a result of
these steps, I am trying to
carry this message to other
addicts, and to practice
these principles in all my
affairs*

Signed   _____

Date   _____

A practical and guided daily journal for anyone in 12 step addiction recovery

Bring consistency and joy to your recovery with daily guidance and encouragement

Your daily blueprint for living a clean and sober life

The Hub of Your Recovery

Space to journal
Practice gratitude
Learn acceptance
Reflection of the day
Spiritual checklist
Plan your day
Step 10/11 daily inventory
Clarity worksheets
Weekly check-ins

12StepJournals

Notes & Reflections

Use these pages to jot down any notes and reflections you may have, or if you need more space as you work through the steps

Notes & Reflections

Notes & Reflections

Notes & Reflections

Notes & Reflections

Notes & Reflections

Notes & Reflections

Notes & Reflections

Notes & Reflections

Notes & Reflections

Notes & Reflections

Notes & Reflections

Notes & Reflections

Notes & Reflections

Notes & Reflections

Notes & Reflections

Notes & Reflections

Notes & Reflections

Notes & Reflections

Notes & Reflections

Notes & Reflections